Helping Doctors Who Manage

Learning from experience

Judith Riley MA, Msc, PCGE, DPhil
Fellow, King's Fund Management College

Published by
King's Fund Publishing
11–13 Cavendish Square
London W1M 0AN

First published 1998

ISBN 1 85717 147 0

A CIP catalogue record for this book is available from the British Library

Distributed by Grantham Book Services Limited
Isaac Newton Way
Alma Park Industrial Estate
GRANTHAM
Lincolnshire
NG31 9SD

Tel: 01476 541 080
Fax: 01476 541 061

Printed and bound in Great Britain by
Biddles Ltd, Guildford and King's Lynn

Cover image: Minuche Mazumdar Farrar

Helping Doctors Who Manage

Learning from experience

Contents

Foreword

Management and medicine in recent times have come to represent a divide with the chasm of 'here be dragons' in between. Doctors who take on management responsibilities find themselves feeling overwhelmed and isolated. They see both sides of the coin but have no one to turn to help them with the difficult and complex situations they face.

In *Helping Doctors Who Manage*, Dr Judith Riley goes some way to help doctors find solutions to wicked problems while bridging the divide between management and medicine in an honest and entertaining way.

Doctors like other professionals learn by telling stories to each other. This book uses real case studies to guide the reader through a range of common dilemmas faced by consultants. Each case study is analysed using management techniques and concepts that many doctors have found genuinely helpful. But this is no ordinary management textbook and the solutions are related to a wider audience in a most potent way.

The stories give a complete living picture rather than a filleted academic skeleton. But do not let the simple chatty style fool you. This is a serious text with an important message. The author has many years' experience of working with clinical consultants who are taking on managerial roles. There are pearls and parables in here which make for fascinating and practical learning. These stories dispel the myths which serve to confuse and contradict.

So, if you are sitting comfortably, why not begin?

Dame Rennie Fritchie
President of the British Association of Medical Managers

Acknowledgements

I am grateful to my colleagues at the King's Fund for teaching me so much, working with me and challenging my ideas. Equally important have been the many doctors who have reacted to my efforts to help them, and in particular I have learned from those who were able to express their difficulties with my approach!

Four of my colleagues provided anecdotes and stories that I have used in this book: Sholom Glouberman, Eva Lauermann, John McClenahan and Peter Mumford.

Sholom is a Canadian, who worked at the King's Fund for several years before returning to Canada. His BA and PhD are in Philosophy. One of his major contributions at the Fund was to help with the design of our Top Manager Programme, which is attended by several doctors each year. He also works on acute hospital organisation.

Eva came to the Fund from top Human Resources jobs in ICI and British Airways, where she was particularly involved in managing major changes. She has run workshops for many clinical director groups and for GP practices, as well as being one of the current directors of the Top Manager Programme.

John joined the Fund from Andersen Consulting, where he worked in a wide range of health, local government and other public sector organisations. Most of his work there included qualitative and quantitative analysis of complex and 'messy' problems, and the planning, development and implementation of information systems. At the Fund he has directed many management courses for consultants and leads sessions that integrate information on finance and clinical effectiveness systems with understanding human motivations.

Peter has worked with trusts as much as with individual clinicians. He has been seconded to three different hospitals, each time for over a year, to help them with major changes. Often he has been able to bring managers and clinicians together. Current work includes developing networks of general practitioners and developing joint courses for GPs and trust consultants.

As the idea for this book began to form, I sent drafts to doctors who had seemed interested in our work for their comments. Every one was most generous with their time, and many wrote me lengthy and legible comments and annotations. I am truly grateful for their enthusiasm, which encouraged me to complete the text. Colleagues and others in similar jobs provided many helpful additions to the text.

CHAPTER 1

Introduction

Working with doctors

During the 1980s the King's Fund was one of the pioneers of encouraging and helping doctors who wanted to learn more about management. Over the last decade we have had over a thousand doctors on our courses, such as 'Management for Consultants', 'Management for Senior Registrars', 'GP Choices', and 'Developing Strategic Agenda for Medical Directors'. Increasingly, we also have doctors on courses that mix professions and organisations, such as our 'Top Manager Programme'. We also run learning sets for small groups and do individual coaching, often for clinical directors.

In contrast to those open-access courses, we have also worked with hundreds more doctors on site, in their own trusts or health authorities. Some of these have meant facilitating 'awaydays' with managers; some were longer programmes of help to clinical directorate staff.

Management development

We call this approach *management development*, as opposed to training or consultancy, to express how we work to enable doctors to think about their own managerial beliefs and practices. Doctors have told us that they have learned from our approach to the benefit of their own teaching, and in Chapter 2 we consider the theoretical and practical background to our work. In addition we look at how this approach differs from traditional medical education and expectations about continuing professional development and discuss some ideas about how people change. Chapter 3 provides a story about consultants reacting to our approach.

Doctors' stories of managing in the NHS

This book is an attempt to share our experience of working with doctors and is written for doctors. It is a book of stories:

- stories that we hear from doctors, when we invite them to tell us about trying to manage and to work with managers;
- stories from our own observations of doctors while working with them over the last ten years.

Doctors' stories of their experiences as managers	Our stories of our experiences as helpers
What it is like to be a doctor-manager	What it is like to be a management developer working with doctors
What problems others have	What helps with a particular problem
Why doctors have such problems with management	What various development methods are like

Figure 1.1 The two kinds of stories and what they contain

I realise that doctors do not expect to read stories as an aid to their work, yet many have told me that this way of expressing their experience is valuable. It may help to think of it as a little like the BMJ's brief anecdotal items 'From Personal Experience'. It is not a textbook on management for doctors, and it is not a report on research.

The doctors' stories of their experiences as managers bring out what it is like to be a doctor-manager. In the discussion of each story I have tried to add any other similar problems that other doctors have told us about. I have also explained the points that doctors say have helped them with the difficulties described.

Each story is taken from reality but has been altered to preserve anonymity and to remove unnecessary details. Most of the quotations used in the stories are the actual words spoken by doctors but some reflect our memories of common reactions in such situations.

The stories we hear are about the difficulties that doctors have when they become clinical or medical directors, lead clinicians, directors of public health or senior partners in GP practices. These problems are often about managing themselves and other doctors and with relationships with other professionals and general managers. Broadly speaking, these stories often seem to focus on five difficult situations:

- time management;
- communication problems;
- difficult people;
- wicked problems;
- personal fears.

Doctors' problems with time management

Doctors often ask for help with time management if they are surveyed on their choice of topics for a management course. Almost all the doctors I have met through the King's Fund have spoken of their stress and attributed it to having too much to do. They have other sources of stress, such as difficult decisions or worries about the quality of services, but it is working long hours and feeling it is never-ending that really seems to be hard. Chapter 4 is focused on such problems.

Doctors' problems with communication

Doctors also bring a variety of difficulties which I would term communication difficulties. We often meet clinical directors who do not trust their managers or each other and who do not expect to work co-operatively with each other. Many senior doctors seem extremely isolated and find it a huge relief to have the chance to share their problems in learning sets. Others come to us for individual coaching, and seem to need as much the space and attention to talk out their plans to an interested face, as any direct advice or coaching. Chapters 5 and 10 are built around stories of difficulties with communication.

Doctors' problems with difficult people

It is very common for doctors to talk of difficult individuals: usually other doctors, but also often senior professionals or managers. They describe these people as having impossible personalities, being lazy or incompetent or self-serving. Few doctors instinctively see themselves as potentially part of any relationship problem. They rarely have any understanding of how one's own personality and needs may affect how one sees and reacts to another person. They have little understanding that people differ and like to work differently and may therefore be expressing this, rather than being awkward for the sake of it. Many of the people doctors have to work with, like the doctors themselves, are presumably also stressed: tired and in a hurry, not too ready to communicate their own problems. Consequently it is all too easy for some of these encounters to go sour and then to assume that the difficulty lies in the other person and is a permanent feature of their character. Chapters 6, 7 and 9 all have stories with elements of 'difficult people'.

Doctors and wicked problems

Many of the situations that doctors bring us, while having a wide variety of presenting problems, seem to me to be of the type we call 'wicked problems' The doctor may say, this is difficult because it is a merger, or its about quality, or getting people to change, yet the conventional wisdom for managing mergers, quality improvement or changing practices does not seem helpful. These problems lie within complex situations of great uncertainty and affecting many interest groups who do not always share the same values. Chapter 8 is particularly about such problems.

Doctors' personal fears

When doctors trust us and feel safe enough to talk about some of their real fears about moving into managerial work, we hear many more personal doubts and difficulties which might be summed up as 'Do I really want to do this?' They expect to become less trusted by peers and to suffer more isolation from having 'Gone over to the enemy'. They worry about their abilities to manage their time with the extra tasks. They worry about their capacity for these new tasks. They worry about the effects of such a step on their longer-term careers, very aware of how easy it is to get out of date. (Later, if they take on a part-time management post, they may worry more about how to give up the excitement and feeling of stimulation, the challenges and the sense of having real power for good that management work can bring!) All the stories include personal elements.

Chapter 11 explores the hypothesis that many of the problems that doctors have with management roles stem from the attitudes that are formed during their clinical training and working lives; managing and doctoring require different approaches and combining the two is incredibly difficult.

Finally, Chapter 12 is a discussion of how a doctor could use the aids to self-development in this book and how to choose the best management development course for an individual's situation and style.

Why I wrote this book

I came to the King's Fund from an academic career, mainly at the Open University, where I was a senior lecturer and head of a group who did R and D on the Open University's teaching materials. I learned a great deal there about how to help adult students to learn and to think in new ways. My interest in working groups began there too, trying to help teams of competitive academics to co-operate over a two-year period to produce new courses and I wrote my PhD about how they prepared their teaching. When I came to the King's Fund in 1987, I learned about many different ways of interacting with our clients, who were all senior managers and professionals in health care: such as coaching, team development, organisation consultancy and learning sets.

I have had doctors in mind as readers while I have been writing. If you have worked with us before, you may find this book an aid to recalling your own thoughts with us. A director of public health, who read the book in draft, said, *'It brought back all sorts of memories, re-visiting was the powerful thing. It brought back the importance of keeping in touch with one's feelings, of having mentors to bounce things off, of not being complacent. There is no-one to challenge me at work.'*

If you are a doctor-manager but have not worked with us, I hope you may find a sense of recognition in my account of other doctors' difficulties. Sometimes, doctors say, *'Just knowing that other doctors are experiencing the same difficulties is enormously helpful. It reduces that awful feeling of isolation'.* Another said, *'Doctors have no-one to tell their stories.'*

Some of the management techniques and ideas that other doctors have valued may be of use to you too. I have tried to explain them in enough detail for you to be able to use them as aids to reflecting on your own situation but they are only aids to reflection: they will not help if applied mechanistically, you have to understand yourself and your situation and be willing to think hard. The final chapter suggests several different ways of supporting your own management development.

If you are contemplating taking on more managerial responsibilities, then the stories may help you anticipate what that may be like. A senior registrar who looked at a draft said, '*It was interesting to see the kind of things I may come across and why my clinical director is being such a pain!*'

Doctors who are interested in medical education have told me that they were helped by the stories about our struggles to help doctors learn and change.

My colleagues and I have varied backgrounds, and we came to this work thinking that we knew a lot about management development. Working with doctors we have gradually come to accept that much management knowledge and many management techniques are of little help with the complex realities of doctors' managerial lives. What does seem to help is to pause before rushing into one's instinctive reaction and to think about management in a different way. Gradually, we are learning how to help doctors to do that essential thinking.

The questions that provoke thought most effectively seem to be:

- What are you feeling and what does that tell you about what's going on?
- Is there anything going on 'under the table' (see page 15)?
- Where are you on the 'change curve' (see page 37)?
- Have you considered all the options for change?
- What would a good doctor-manager do now?
- What have you failed to ask or communicate?
- Are you trying to rush into a decision or action too soon?
- Is this your responsibility and could anyone else help you?
- Are you managing up, down and outwards?
- Are you paying attention to all the channels of communication (see page 77)?

The chapters that follow describe these and other ways of provoking reflection in more detail. Most management development happens without formal interventions such as management courses or workshops: on the job, by chance and opportunistic learning from experience. I am quite sure that this is the most usual and the most powerful route and our own work tries to recognise that and to use our short time with doctors to sharpen the focus, to ensure that experience is used and its lessons learned.

CHAPTER 2

Working with Doctors

Over the years, by listening to those doctors with whom we have had the privilege to work, we have discovered some good ways of helping doctors to learn about management. We are still learning and, as the next chapter shows, we certainly have not yet got all the answers. However, many doctors have been pleased with the effectiveness of our methods for their ostensible purpose, and some have also told us that they have learned about our methods of education with interest. Consequently, in this chapter, I want to explain what may seem an unusual approach and why, in many ways, we have chosen to break with the usual academic traditions.

Our approach can be summarised as follows:

- *reality-based*, including the reality of here and now;
- giving attention to the whole *individual* person;
- focusing on *development* rather than training.

Reality based

We centre our work with doctors on their real managerial agendas, rather than on examples of potential concerns or generalised case studies. Often we will use entirely open agendas, or we may introduce an area (e.g. dealing with difficult people, or strategic planning) from our experience of many doctors' concerns. We encourage much of the work on the topic to focus on the real specifics of each individual doctor's work. We treat our knowledge of management as a resource of theories, concepts and techniques that may be helpful and we offer it flexibly, as it seems to be needed. We try to use common-sense language, specifically related to the doctors' situations.

There are now several books which draw from management knowledge, illustrating it with clinical examples. While these are more accessible than texts written for business people, or general managers in health care, we do not find them wholly satisfactory. They tend to be based on a mechanistic control model of management, whose limitations are increasingly being realised. We try to reverse their approach, which we can do because we work almost entirely face to face with small groups. So rather than focusing on somewhat abstract management knowledge, we try to focus on the specific individual experience of doctors acting in management roles.

This focus on reality seems to us to be important for two reasons. First, the reality of doctors is exceedingly complex (see Chapter 8 on wicked problems) and most management theory is not designed for this degree of complexity. Rather it has been developed from and for commercial business which, however difficult, is almost certainly less complex than the dilemmas continually faced by doctors. There is a thread of new management theory which is designed for such difficult situations but it is not yet sufficiently developed to be terribly useful.

Working with reality means that we have to create an environment in which doctors feel safe to share confidential material, both with us and with other colleagues with whom they are working. We ask groups if they are willing to treat everything that they may hear as confidential while working with us. This agreement is readily given; doctors do seem able to trust us with confidential material about individuals or plans about their places of work. As one Medical Director said, *'That is what made our sessions so valuable. You knew you could talk with and in confidence.'*

Second, it is unreasonable to expect doctors to transfer management ideas themselves, from examples to their own situations. They are very busy and any course or session is likely to get pushed to the back of the literal or metaphorical shelf in their office. If we pre-digest and sieve relevant ideas for a specific real situation that they are facing, they experience the power of management knowledge to help them. Then motivation to use such knowledge on subsequent occasions is much more powerful.

An example

Many doctors now have to lead or work in multi-disciplinary teams, with perhaps, nurses, professions allied to medicine, health care managers and social work managers. Team relationships are complex but most management theory assumes that work-teams are all employed by the same organisation in some hierarchical structure with the team-leader as either formally the boss or appointed with authority given by a boss. In such a situation, team members expect to be told what to do and know that they can be sacked if they do not do it.

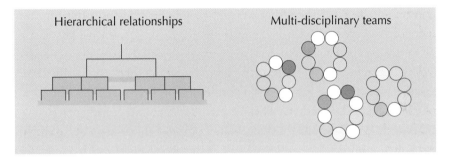

Figure 2.1 Team relationships

Years ago, we used to digest and offer this team theory for doctors, somewhat apologetically. Doctors seemed to enjoy our lectures, carefully prepared with overheads and handouts and clapped politely at the end but it was clear from their questions that it was not going to be easy for them to apply that knowledge to their own situations. Indeed they concentrated on playing with the ideas as ideas, rather than making any attempt to transfer them to improve their own teams. Tim Scott, a senior fellow at BAMM (The British Association of Medical Managers), suggested to me that *'doctors are quick to smell out that management theory is like medicine in the 19th century, with both poor reliability and validity'*.

Now we start with sharing stories, encouraging the doctors to describe their teams and what they see as their difficulties. They commonly cite:

- shifting members and purposes;
- conflicting interests;
- unclear lines of authority;
- histories of difficulties between professions and stereotypical behaviour patterns.

We can often also get through to doctors' emotional difficulties. We ask them to take five minutes to make a list of the differences between good and bad doctor leaders or team members, from their own years of experience. They can do this and you can see reflection on their own situations in their eyes. We then run through a tiny selection of possibly helpful ideas, having discarded sheets of notes while they were speaking, reordering and rephrasing our suggestions in terms of the specific problems raised by this group of doctors. We offer far fewer ideas from management literature than we used to, but those few are focused and relevant to what we have just heard. Using this approach also encourages doctors to feel more in control of the teaching situation and to join in with us, offering their own ideas to each other.

We then circle back to their own reality, by asking them to consider both the few ideas that we have offered and their own lists of the characteristics of good and bad team leadership or membership, and consider their own behaviour in relation to that material. They end the session by talking in pairs, being self-critical and noticing their own strengths as team leaders or members with surprise.

Tapping into an existing resource

Ideally, we might be able to do much of this work with doctors in their own teams, or by studying in teams drawn from different professions and organisations. While we do this whenever we can, it is often still too strange to be acceptable for many doctors, or they feel too uncertain, too exposed in such situations.

One part of doctors' reality is that they are managing so much in their clinical work. By the time we meet doctors, they have many years of experience of leading others and managing themselves, others' work and often budgets. We try to get them to activate this resource. The key seems to be to get a group trying to help each other, an easy behaviour pattern for doctors, once we can get them to put aside the assumption that 'it's education today', so the appropriate behaviour is to be passive.

Following through a series of exercises that ask them to share their stories of how awful it is, and the differences between good and bad management by doctors they know, leads them painlessly into this more active use of their own experience. We get comments such as the consultant who said, '*It is not like learning to be a doctor, I already know a lot of this. It's just about applying it.*' Our task is to help them to mobilise the resources that they already have, as much as to add any new ideas.

When we ask them to transfer those clinical managerial skills to their new part-time management roles, somehow that feels difficult. While a doctor may manage patients or juniors well, this skill does not always instinctively transfer to managing their peers, or other senior professionals. A colleague told me of working with a small group of consultants, who had been discussing influencing people, giving feedback, and delegating, and who had given a lot of attention to examples of staff who did not do what they had agreed to do. Then they began to see it:

> '*This is what we do every day of our lives. You are reframing our existing skills, that we've developed with patients, to dealing with colleagues. It feels shaky because we haven't got that power relationship that we rely on with patients and we don't feel we are clearly the expert. Patients won't challenge us or give us any unpleasant feedback…*'

Another aspect of a reality-based approach is summed up in the old teacher's phrase, 'You have to start from where they are'. In many cases, when we first meet doctors, they are expecting a form of work with us that fits their previous experience of either education or consultancy. So they expect us to play the expert, to lead, to lecture, to know (or claim to know) the answers. We often want to behave differently from these expectations and we need the doctors to join us in actively bringing their own real-life experiences forward. We have to allow an accommodation period – a time for adjustment of expectations, and different people will need different amounts of adjustment time. The story in Chapter 3 shows an example of two consultants on a management course, who were honest about their difficulty in adjusting to our novel demands.

Working experientially

A final aspect of being based in reality, is that we work experientially. That means that whatever happens when we are with doctors, is good learning material. If we are on our toes, we will try to use it, as a shared experience that is fresh in our minds it should be a very powerful learning opportunity.

We had a management consultant in to run a session on some new ideas he had about time management. He gave an interesting introduction, all about how different people visualised time differently: some seeing the past as behind them, for example, while others saw time as moving in front of them from left to right, so that the past was way over on their left-hand side. After a while he seemed to be losing the interest of the group: there was a lot of shuffling and leaning back in chairs and some people were openly reading papers in their folders, or their post.

At the tea-break, the two faculty present discreetly checked this out and then suggested that we split the group, so that those who wanted more theory could carry on with the lecturer, while the rest could focus on their own difficulties in managing their time and look at how his ideas illuminated those problems. When the lecturer had gone, with many polite thanks from the group, one said, *'I learned more from how you handled that, than I did from the session itself'.*

The ensuing discussion ranged around not only the management of other people who were going on too long at meetings, but also how we preferred to be managed ourselves, and led us into a debate about getting and giving feedback which took over much of the afternoon at the group's insistence. The freshness of the shared experience gave this discussion more impact, we believe, than any pre-planned session on feedback could have achieved. It was real and specific, and we had all been involved in it.

Attention to the whole individual person

Doctors are used to an emphasis on the rational, analytical approach. Much of their training and the emphasis on evidence-based medicine push them in that direction. However, they know that their work involves much more than attention to clinical evidence: there is an art to it too. We have to ask them to use that ability which goes beyond the rational, logical and scientific to help them to be better managers. They can readily agree that when they are managing patients or relatives, they have to pay attention to much more than the surface of what is said.

Most of them are skilled in observing and using body language and are aware of many levels of communication in a consultation.

We point out that those 'forces' are at play when managing staff too. The following figure indicates some of what may be going on at a meeting to discuss cover for a sick colleague.

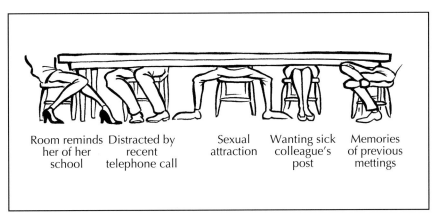

| Room reminds her of her school | Distracted by recent telephone call | Sexual attraction | Wanting sick colleague's post | Memories of previous mettings |

Figure 2.2 The forces under the table at a meeting

We have probably all been in meetings where we think we are observing keenly what is going on, but we are then surprised when the obvious does not happen: the debate is suddenly blocked or veers off at a tangent. In the lower part of the figure, I am suggesting that there are many layers of things going on 'under the table', as it were. Although we all know that these forces exist, we often ignore them in our analyses. For example, there may be a past history of good or poor work together, something said may remind a member of something else, one member may have come into the meeting totally distracted by a recent phone call.

We also emphasise how doctors are themselves a part of whatever they are managing, rather than separate from it. This is easy to see when we are working with them, perhaps reviewing a meeting where we have been observers. They may be led to see how their own feelings and recent experience leaked out in the meeting. From their shared and recent experience, they can usually accept that their feelings may have been read by others and possibly misread too.

Those emotions may be considered as clues: clues to doctors' own reactions and clues to what others may be feeling. Rather than putting one's own feelings aside as irrelevant, we suggest that doctors who want to enhance their managerial abilities should pay attention to their own emotions and use them as data.

Individuals have different preferences in how they learn: some like to start with an overview, while others prefer to build towards that through understanding the basics. Some like to start with theory and some with practical examples. Some prefer to discuss new ideas with others and find that it is in talking that they can discover the gaps in their understanding, while others need time alone, a quiet space to reflect. There is a large literature on such models of individual preferences in learning (e.g. Kolb, 1984; Myers, 1993) but the point for us is that we must allow for such differences. If we are working with a group of doctors we have to offer a variety of different ways of learning over any session. We will try to ensure that individual preferences can be met, particularly when working on something delicate, such as relationships between directorates, or merging services, by suggesting that individuals choose the method that suits them best from a set of given approaches. However, this is an area where I believe we still need to be more creative.

Development as well as training

I have four cartoons each showing a different relationship between the doctors and the King's Fund fellow.

The expert

In the first cartoon, the 'expert' is desperately trying to squeeze things into a suitcase and the doctors do not appear in the picture at all. The 'expert' is focused on the material contents which he wants to convey, it all feels important and the time limits are a terrible frustration. The 'expert' is focused on the material contents which he wants to convey, it all feels important and the time limits are a terrible frustration. The 'expert' is hooked on the ideas, or determined to appear up-to-date. What might be best for the doctors does not feature in his concerns. If he thinks of them at all, it is to hope they don't interrupt and that they arrive on time! The doctors' role is very passive: they are there to listen and take notes,

Figure 2.3 The expert

aiming to transfer the 'expert's' material from his voice into their brains, probably to retain it in that form until it is needed.

Many doctors have experienced this kind of teaching from some of their more inexperienced lecturers at medical school and they expect something similar when they meet with us. They know it is silly to expect to learn how to be a good manager in the short time we have together, just a short course or a few meetings over a year or two but that is all they can afford and all that is on offer. They expect to be passive, to collect up the handouts and put them on a shelf.

The following images of plants and jugs make the point that we do not see doctors as identical jugs who have to be filled up by us with management knowledge. Rather, we see doctors as plants – we may be able to add a little fertiliser but the growth is individual and depends on many other factors.

Figure 2.4 Jugs or plants?

It is very tempting for us to use jug-filling and 'expert' models, for we all enjoy displaying our knowledge and have our vulnerabilities, especially when working in front of colleagues, as we often do. And doctors easily slide into colluding with this urge in us to be the 'experts', even when this is not helpful. Obviously, the model has its uses: we do have an expertise in management knowledge, but management knowledge on its own is not enough.

The entertainer

In the second cartoon, I am the clown, trying to entertain the audience of doctors. They are represented as guinea pigs, because in my efforts to entertain them, I am constantly trying new ideas to catch their attention, new buzz words, new teaching techniques. So there will be a stream of funny stories and telling anecdotes, and my acting various roles in front of a still passive audience. The doctors' role is to be amused, to enjoy and to appreciate me, for in this model I want to be loved above all. They must clap and complete their evaluation forms with appreciative comments because they have had such a good time. Adult party bags, in the form of nicely produced handouts will be expected and provided. Doctors will doubtless also remember some of the key points, but many may be lost in the excitement of the trimmings.

Doctors have usually experienced this model of the relationship, both at medical school and at more recent conferences. They have enjoyed it and they may hope for something similar from the King's Fund, as they may have heard colleagues describe working with us as 'most enjoyable'.

Figure 2.5 The entertainer

Doctors can easily get bored and then often become critical. When we are designing events or courses for doctors, we do indeed consider entertainment and what will be enjoyed but not as sufficient in itself. Group work is nearly always enjoyed if properly structured and is a powerful means of development because it involves sharing experience. Entertaining examples can be importantly memorable.

For instance, rather than explaining the concept of espoused theories and theories in use (Argyris and Schön, 1996) in the abstract, I always start with acting out taking my small daughter shopping with her pocket money. She gets £1.50 a week and my espoused theory, which I explain to her, is that pocket money is to spend on whatever she likes. She often asks me to take her to Woolworth's on a Saturday. When she hovers over the sweet counter, I look at my watch, hand on hip, *'You had a lot of sweets yesterday, remember. Let's go and look at the toys first before you decide.'* My manipulative manner always makes the doctors laugh as I display my 'theory in use': disapproving her choice of purchase. This distinction then often recurs in subsequent conversations about doctors' motivations.

Figure 2.6 The engineer

The 'engineer'

The third cartoon shows the teacher as an engineer, designing railway tracks through difficult countryside for the little trains, who are the doctor-students of management. She knows where her trains begin their journey the state of their knowledge and skills when they start work together. She knows the summit platform, where they all wish to be and they are agreed upon their objectives for the learning, the endpoint. She knows the terrain through which they must travel, where the difficult stretches and corners are. Her task is to devise the track, to keep the gradient of learning reasonable, to keep the trains away from steep drops (avoid difficult questions) and to get them to their pre-arranged endpoint on time at the end of their journey.

Doctors know about this kind of teaching too – courses or workshops with objectives at the start and sometimes assessment at the end, often skills training. They have met this both at medical school from well-organised, experienced lecturers and in continuing medical education.

If their model of management is that there is a series of technical skills and areas of knowledge to be learned, then this may be their expectation of our teaching.

We might use this approach in teaching a skill, such as assertiveness. We might ask individual doctors to practice a difficult conversation several times:

- the first time they try it, we might suggest they raise and firm their voice;
- the second time that they lean forward in their chair at their full height;
- the third time that they state their aim for the meeting in the first sentence, and so on.

Thus the learning is broken down into manageable steps, the teacher knowing the six or seven points which 'should' be learned in advance of the students.

Adults working together

The fourth and last cartoon shows management developer and doctors as adults, working together. The developer may be the facilitator or guide, with the hat, but other members of the group also bring resources, such

Figure 2.7 The facilitator

as a map or their own guidebook. Some doctors can set out on their own journey without the guide. Her expectation would be that there would be several groups moving off and some would walk alone. Each would be pursuing their own chosen aims and using a combination of their own resources, with possibly a little help initially or at intervals from their facilitator. The model asks a lot of the guide: it is hard to maintain one's confidence in the face of a reluctant group and easy to retreat to a more controlling method. The guide must also resist judgemental instincts: she must participate in the mutual respect as an equal as well as an enabler.

This model of learning is not one which is familiar to most doctors, or rather is not familiar to them under that label. They do have this model but they do not keep it in the mental file labelled 'how teaching and learning happen'. It is, of course, how they have developed most of their life, informally, and how they have had to face most of the challenges that they meet at work, although they may not instinctively look to others to share their journeys or to offer them additional resources. It is a model that is familiar to many GPs, who know the value of working in this way with their patients. When other doctors try this, they also discover new pleasures from others' different interests and are helped to overcome some of their difficulties by others' different approaches. At the end of the course or workshop, the participants are tired but jubilant: they have worked hard and are satisfied.

We emphasise this fourth facilitator model at the King's Fund, because it seems particularly suited to working with people of our own age, who are highly expert in their own fields, used to leadership and to trying to help others. However, it may be culturally dependent and does not always work as readily cross-culturally. For example, a group of Spanish doctor-chief executives found the concept of sharing problems or trying to help other chief executives quite alien and disturbing for several weeks. Under stress, they reverted to working alone, and some never felt comfortable with our approach.

The need to be flexible

When we are preparing to work with doctors, we often find that we go through each of these models and keep elements that each suggests in our final choices.

- We will discuss what we think we have to offer to the situation (*expert model*).
- We will consider what we think the doctors will want and need and then we may turn to sequencing and pacing our initial ideas (*engineer model*).
- We will invent and recall interesting exercises and pictures and look for a variety of learning methods and of speakers to make it as enjoyable as possible (*entertainer model*).
- Before we finish, we always return to the need to be flexible, to join the doctors on their journey, which must start from where we find they are, pursue their interests and use the resources we find among them. In this way we usually enter into the frame of mind of the guide (*facilitator model*).

The four models

Role of teacher	Role of doctors/students
Expert Up to date, knowledgeable Cover the ground	**Invisible** Irrelevant, passive spectators
Entertainer Quick, varied, funny Sole performer	**Invited** Guinea-pigs, audience Appreciative
Engineer In charge, the designer of route and of instructions	**Inanimate** Follow instructions mechanically
Facilitator One resource among many	**Independent** Active, resourceful, offering help, taking responsibility

---

Taking responsibility

The approach described so far is contrary to many of most doctors' expectations: It uses doctors' existing own and group experience of managing and insists on them taking responsibility for their own learning. Whether they come to us on a course, or are invited to some kind of meeting with us, doctors expect a more passive, expert-led, knowledge-based approach. They do not expect to be involved in any emotional way and they do not expect to be asked to expose anything of their own managerial life and especially not their own reactions to that life.

The unfamiliarity of starting work with us is often a shock and produces reactions of impatience and confusion at first. A radiologist who joined one of our courses said,

> *'I was struck by the difference in educational methods. I remember being unable to tell colleagues what I had learned, unlike my radiology CME courses, where I would come away with new techniques and facts to apply. Three months later a superintendent who knew me well commented that I was different, I never got upset by things now. I think that is the end product of this experiential style: more understanding of self, others and the system.'*

We believe that we have enough experience now to be sure that this approach is a good one for many people, in the judgement of our customers, the doctors themselves. However, this is rarely their initial judgement. While we have a strong respect for their judgement, we often have to take a risk and ask doctors to give us the benefit of the doubt for a while when they start working with us. The story in Chapter 3 illustrates this reaction and some of the development associated with it.

The story in Chapter 4 shows us working in a combination of 'engineer' and 'facilitator' mode with a group of medical directors who needed a lot of different techniques to enable them to get to grips with their individual sets of priorities. Each was also able to voice their individual motivations for taking on the job and to share some of the feelings of frustration that most were suffering.

Chapter 5 is based on experiential work, using clinical directors' reactions to each other, including emotional reactions and their body language, in their meeting with us. The work was entirely based in their recent and current realities of failures of communication, which we were able to help them to face and deal with in their own individual ways.

Chapter 6 is again based on experiential, individual and reality-based work, with my colleague working confidentially with one clinical director. His energy was focused on offering her possible interpretations of her own behaviour, for her to accept or reject as she found fit.

Chapter 7 begins with a story about coaching, where my colleague acted as facilitator, individualising his suggestions of techniques that the GP might use to analyse her own difficulties with her career and her colleagues.

Chapter 8 starts with the story of a facilitated learning set, where the main work of helping an individual with his real-time problems is done by the other doctors in the group.

In Chapter 9 the story has an element of the 'engineer' model, in that my colleague there had a clear aim for the session and knew that she had to take the group through a series of steps, avoiding some tricky patches, if they were to get what they wanted from the session. However, she was also working experientially: drawing their attention to how events, while they were working together, were illustrating the ideas which she was trying to convey to them.

Chapter 10 is another individualised story with a colleague acting flexibly to help a consultant who had difficulties in communicating with others. At some stages other doctors gave her feedback drawing on her behaviour with them. There were never clear objectives in advance, the work proceeded opportunistically and under the control of the doctor concerned.

References

Argyris C, Schön D. *Organizational Learning II: Theory, method and practice.* Reading (Mass.): Addison Wesley, 1996

Myers I Briggs, with Myers PB. *Gifts Differing: Understanding Personality Type.* Palo Alto (CA): Consulting Psychologists Press Books, 1993

Kolb D. *Experiential Learning: Experience as the source of learning and development.* Englewood Cliffs (NJ): Prentice Hall, 1984

CHAPTER 3

The Angry
Consultants

What follows is the first of the stories that make up the main body of
this book. It is included to show how our approach to the development
of doctors is demanding of them. It is an unfamiliar approach, which
occasionally produces reactions of shock and confusion, allied with
criticism and impatience. At times like these we need all our strength
to hang on to what we believe will provide what is needed, rather than
give in and provide what is wanted. At the same time we have to keep
questioning whether we are right – we must not unthinkingly assume
that 'we know best what's good for you'.

T his story focuses on the morning of the second day of a week-long course for consultants. We start each day with a brief review session and on this occasion I had asked everyone to think about what they had learned the day before. I had also asked them to reflect on what they had done that might have helped or hindered their own, or others' learning, knowing that several had already expressed interest in the way we were working with them. Most people settled happily into quiet thought, making notes and then sharing them with a partner, as I had suggested.

Two silent men

The room looked busy and animated, apart from one corner. Two men were sitting alone at a round table for five, they were silent and looked as if they were waiting for the session to be over. The rest of the group did not challenge this behaviour. If they noticed them at all, they clearly expected this to be my job to sort.

I went over to the two of them and, trying not to be too challenging, asked if the questions were clear. I said that I could see they were not happy, just by looking at them.

One was angry

There was a reluctant silence, then one burst out with a grumpy, *'I can't answer your questions as I did not learn anything yesterday.'* I sat down with them, asking him to go on, trying hard to bring all of my attention and myself, including my uncertainty, to this discussion. With a few more prompts, it came pouring out: *'I am extremely busy at work and when I finish here I am going into work and then home to my family, and yesterday I sat here for seven hours and it was a complete waste of time. It was appallingly slow and there was nothing there, just a load of playing about.'*

I listened

I kept prompting, and he kept repeating himself. I repeated my appreciation of how hard it must be to do so much and to get away. I said that in his shoes, I could honestly say that I would probably feel just the same. I did not tell him how guilty I felt, how unreasonable I saw our demands as being. After a while, perhaps somewhat relieved of his feelings by voicing them and perhaps realising that I was listening and had heard him, he began to be able to hear himself and to qualify what he was saying.

> 'Yes, I can see that the others seem to be happy with it but I'm too busy for that, I'm doing three jobs and I haven't time for this kind of thing. I can see that I may not be bringing my best attention here and it is hard to stop and think but I still blame the teaching. Yes, I would have preferred lectures, that would have been easier for me.'

I said it must be hard for him to learn new things, while so full of these feelings of resentment. I felt I was walking a tightrope between seeming uncertain, weak and not worth bothering with, and on the other side, seeming patronising and blaming him for his reaction.

The other was disappointed

The second consultant had been sitting quietly through this but now came in with, *'It's not like that for me, I'm new to this job and I haven't done any management training before but my wife is a manager and she asked me last night what we had learned and I had to just say it was common sense, really. So, I do feel rather disappointed so far.'* Rather unhelpfully, I repeated what had been pointed out several times the previous day, that there were really no easy answers, that managing in the NHS was extremely difficult. I wondered if he might now feel more comfortable, having dissociated himself from the angry consultant.

They were responsible for their own learning

We were running out of time and my colleague had arrived to take the next session, so I had to leave them there, asking them to bear with it if they could, but to opt out and vote with their feet, if they were sure it was not for them. In doing this I was trying to reinforce the idea that they were responsible for their own learning and sitting back and blaming teacher passively was not a sensible option.

By the third morning those two angry consultants were smiling sheepishly at us and participating in the work. At the end of the week, they were both feeling much more positive: the young consultant said, *'I have learned about a new form of education and that is really important for me. I am going to teach differently from now on.'* The other said, *'I came on this programme feeling jagged and exhausted and I now feel that I can make changes and sort out my life.'*

Positive attitudes emerged

––––––––––––––––––––––– DISCUSSION –––––––––––––––––––––––

What had we been doing on the Monday? We had begun with a slow session of introductions, aiming to get everyone settled and to mark a different pace of work here. We were trying to begin the process of refocusing them from the 'teacher' up front, to the group, as a resource for them: sitting them at small round tables in an informal layout and asking them to spend most of the session listening to each other rather than to us. We had also explained our approach to the development of doctors in several different ways, including the cartoons in Chapter 2.

This is a session that we discuss endlessly when designing these courses; there is always the tension between starting reasonably, from where the doctors are, and setting new expectations. After coffee we had tried to redress the balance by offering a lecture in a more familiar format, with a simple overview of what was happening to the NHS and why NHS managing was bound to be difficult.

Then one of my colleagues had run a double session about strategic planning, where she had introduced several techniques, including two that are deceptively simple but usually prove very helpful to doctors:

• forcefield analysis (Lippitt and Lippitt, 1986);
• stakeholder analysis, taken from a technique called 'commitment planning' (Beckhard and Harris, 1987).

We had given them time and encouragement to apply these techniques to their own situations at work and to discuss the results.

Forcefield analysis

Forcefield analysis asks one to list out all the forces, influences and sources of power that are on one's side: that are acting to help achieve whatever change one is wishing to make. Forces that may act against one's plans are then listed as an opposing group. It may be possible to give some indication of the relative strengths of some of the forces, or to see that some balance each other out.

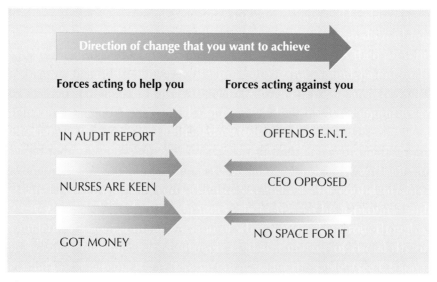

Figure 3.1 Forcefield analysis

Stakeholder analysis

Stakeholder analysis is equally simple:

- it asks one to list all those individuals or groups who have a stake, an interest, in one's plans;
- then one categorises their present positions into one or other of the columns in the diagram;
- finally, one marks which column one needs them to move into.

Stakeholders	Present positions and Desired positions		
	active opposition	*neutral*	*active support*
CEO	X ───────────────────────► X		
Medical Director		X	
Nurses			X
MP		X ──────► X	
ENT	X ──────► X		

Figure 3.2 Stakeholder analysis

Not surprisingly, what one often finds is that one is uncertain of some key players' views and the technique prompts one to go back and pursue this information. Sometimes people are surprised to discover that very few key players have to shift their views and the analysis prompts a focusing down of one's persuasive efforts.

These two techniques are extremely simple; so simple that calling them 'techniques' seems to make too much of them. We offer them as opportunities to provoke thought, if given a chance. When applied to a managerial problem as analytical tools, they are often surprisingly revealing. Doctors often say later,

> 'I have learned that it is worth analysing my problems'. 'Those simple techniques, like forcefield, look like nothing but I know I shall use that again and again.' 'I need to get others to want to do it for me!' 'I had never thought of sorting out people like that [stakeholders], I used to assume I had to get everyone on my side, now I can see it need not be that heavy.' 'I only have to move a few people from blocking me to letting it happen and I can do that…' 'I never thought that logic wasn't enough to win my argument.'

Avoiding the 'passive' mode

When I checked with my colleagues later, I discovered as I had suspected, that these two disaffected consultants had not tried to apply these techniques in the session the day before our conversation. They had understood the concepts immediately and had thought that was enough: they were still in passive mode. Application must have seemed a very odd request to all the doctors in the room, despite my colleagues' best efforts to explain what was wanted. They had little energy for experimentation and it is not surprising that some of them failed to hear this instruction to apply the ideas and were unaware that they had not played their positive and essential part.

One of the most difficult and useful lessons of this kind of work, we are told, is this need to slow down and engage the brain and work at management development, or a management problem at work. So many doctors are so busy these days that they do not have a moment to think and for much of their days are mentally running as fast as they can, almost on automatic pilot. Coming into a slow-paced development day can be totally maddening, impossibly frustrating.

We have yet to find satisfactory ways of achieving a switch of pace, without triggering a switch off into social leisure time mode. Perhaps we should draw a parallel with the doctors' dilemma when faced with patients who know what they want, regardless of the doctors' expertise: the mother wanting grommets for the child with glue ear, or cough medicine? Perhaps we should make the switch a more gradual one? Discussing this problem with Tim Scott of BAMM, he said, *'It's OK to turn up for tennis and find it's badminton, but not chess!'*

A sense of control

We were lucky enough to have five days with these doctors and there was time for them to unwind a bit and to experience real changes in their attitudes. Many said that they had regained some positive sense of control over their working lives. You will have noticed in this story, that one of the problems was the angry consultant's workload and his stress. He had assumed he could benefit from the course by giving it only a small amount of his energy – being present would be enough. Presumably, he had not found much of his previous education needed more than this. Indeed, the word training can be a signal to switch off one's brain.

The approach of learning by working on real problems from their own experience seems to be so foreign to some, that it can take several days for the message to sink in. They think that they are giving the course appropriate attention, because they are following their model of education and they cannot see why there are long pauses after each input from the staff. They cannot hear that they are being asked to follow a different model and to behave in a different, more active way. When the passive mode produces little gain, they blame the course at first. Gradually, they notice that other doctors are busy and enthusiastic and gradually the repeated messages from us about applying what we offer, sink in. We try to mix them up, so that those who are finding it hard to engage are soon sat with a doctor who has caught on and is enthusiastically working on his own experience. Working with a group makes it difficult to adjust the pace of the demands to each individual doctor's needs.

A 'competence trap'

One factor that makes almost any kind of learning difficult for senior doctors is that they are so very successful – they are in what March &

Olsen call a 'competence trap' (March and Olsen, 1976). It is hard for them to admit any incompetence or to open themselves up to new ideas in any real sense of making a difference to what they believe or do, for are their old ways not tried and proven effective? A consultant told me that in her view, *'Doctors don't like to admit any kind of incompetence or insufficiency, or accept even constructive criticism'*. Another said, *'Some doctors find it difficult to ask colleagues about new techniques or to go for teaching.'*

Presumably such attitudes are learned in clinical training and from their role models of senior colleagues at work. They are trained to be individualists: to become consultants who will lead firms, teach others and accept that the buck stops with them.

There is often a strong flavour of impending emotional involvement or personal challenge in this work with us, which may well raise defences for a while. I wonder if, for some doctors, learning itself may have unfortunate associations from their past, where being a student meant being very tired and worried, and learning was often a humiliating process, rather than a matter of self-directed problem solving. They may well have a disinclination to return to that struggle; courses may have an association with their past potential for failure.

Awareness of one's own reactions

It is quite common for one or two members of a group of doctors working with us to show the feelings that were illustrated in this story, and doubtless several others will be hiding their negative reactions. We try to 'read' our participants all the time, staying alert to their reactions and putting our own feelings aside. We can then use our observations to help those on the course to notice how feelings are often so clearly expressed in 'body language':

* postures;
* voices;
* expressions.

I remember coaching a doctor who, whenever I asked him a question, closed his eyes and tipped his chair onto its back legs. When I asked if hewas aware of this, he was quite startled. He had not consciously known what he was doing and could see immediately that this would not produce the reaction he wanted in many situations. Doctors say things like,

'I realise I look at my notes in meetings or at the chair, and only rarely do I watch the other members to see what they are thinking.' 'I just didn't realise how much you can tell from observing people, yet I do it all the time with my patients. I do have the skills for this, I just had not thought of applying them to watching my staff or the managers.'

Doctors are always surprised at our insistence that they should make themselves aware of their own emotional reactions to managing. They can understand the rational case, that feelings may get in the way, but they have had long years of having to put their own emotions aside, in order to be able to deal with the often painful realities of their jobs. It is strange to them at first to learn to use their feelings as a source of useful information.

I was pretty sure that having expressed their anger, even in this restrained way, the two consultants in the story would feel a little better. You cannot move on if you have too much 'unfinished business' in your mind. You cannot think about the future if you are bogged down in the past or the present.

For example, we often talk about endings and how people react to them differently: either running away from them, or pretending that they are not happening and how hard it can be to make an appropriate closure. Doctors have made comments such as, *'It was really useful just to know that others felt the same, had the same kind of difficulties. I hadn't expected that. I feel much better now and ready to get on with things.'*

Later it might be possible to refer back to this time and get the first angry man to use it as a means to better understanding himself and possibly questioning whether he wanted to continue to manage his time in this way. We might be able to return to why the second man felt disappointed rather than angry and whether that was a pattern he had at work too. We are trying to observe emotional reactions, while we work with doctors, and trying to help them to see whether there is anything to be learned for the benefit of their work, from their behaviour on a course with us while away from work. We are then using experiential learning: learning directly from their individual experience, as observed by both them and their 'teacher'. However, too much reflection and analysis might become self-criticism to the degree that it destroys the essential confidence that all consultants must cultivate to be able to do their jobs.

Occasionally, we meet a differently caused form of anger: that which is transferred from another situation. For example, when special health authorities (SHAs)were being threatened by reforms to their funding around 1990, we were asked to provide several workshops for newly forming SHA clinical directorates. We designed events which asked them to work together, with our help, on their futures: reviewing their clinical activities and how they wished these to develop and what sources and levels of funding could be expected for these. Many of the directorate teams felt so threatened by the uncertainties and so angry at the direction of government policy, that they could not engage with this work. We became the scapegoats for their anger, which may have helped relieve their feelings a little but did not allow them to make much progress with the rethinking of their futures, that the hospital managers had wanted for them. Our attempts to get round the problem were unsuccessful, we had misjudged the situation. Maybe it would have been better to have waited another year and then we might not have wasted their time and money.

In other groups, doctors have spoken of their anger at government policy but not been so overwhelmed with it. Then it has been possible to help them by providing an analysis of the changing context of their work. One of my colleagues working with GPs was told that, *That's the first time I've ever understood what's going on and why I'm so angry'*.

The dilemma with that kind of overview is the danger of being so simplistic that one is boring. Yet sometimes telling people what they already know can be very powerful: the essence of the powerful insight is often that doctors suddenly find words for what they have experienced and felt but have been unable to express.

Responding to change

We often introduce the idea of the 'change curve' (Marris, 1992), which expresses the common emotional changes that occur with imposed change.

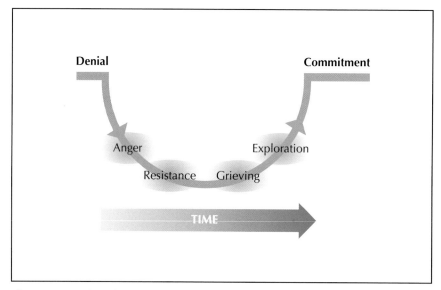

Figure 3.3 'The change curve'

This says that people commonly experience denial of the reality of the change at first, followed by anger at what is being done to them and, often, resistance. Only when these two stages have been lived through, will there be any chance to move on into exploring the possibilities of the change and making some kind of commitment to it. We encourage doctors to ask themselves where they, or others at work, are on this curve.

Another useful idea is that when one feels stuck in an impossible situation and all the possible analysis of the situation, its causes and one's own reactions to it have yielded no solutions, one still always has at least four options to consider:

- seek to change the situation;
- change oneself and, in particular, how one lets it affect oneself;
- put up with it;
- get out.

These options were drawn to the two consultants' attention and, in the end, they chose to change themselves.

In the rest of this book, each chapter offers more stories of doctors working with us. There are occasional difficulties described but most of our experience has been positive. We are still learning and we have to live with the knowledge that we have chosen an approach to working with doctors that has inherent risks. It can help in powerful ways and it will always be rejected by a few, leaving feelings of failure for us to absorb. However, doctors' politeness and ability to hide their reactions may save us from a great deal of pain!

References

Beckhard R, Harris RT. *Organizational Transitions: Managing complex change.* Reading (Mass.): Addison Wesley, 1987

Lippitt G, Lippitt R. *The consulting process in action.* 2nd edn. La Jolla (CA): University Associates, 1986

March JG, Olsen G. *Ambiguity and Choice in Organisations.* Bergen (Norway): Universitetsforlaget, 1976

Marris P. *Loss and Change.* London: Routledge, 1992

CHAPTER 4

There Is Far
Too Much To Do

The following story is about a session on setting priorities among a group of medical directors, who had been invited to a three-day workshop some years ago, to think through what was then a new role. (Flux and Riley, 1994). The story illustrates what seems to be an almost universal problem for doctors: time management.

There were 16 medical directors on this, the first workshop. They were the clinical leaders of a wide range of trusts, including both hospitals and community services. Some were new to the role and some had been medical directors for several years. While some found BAMM (British Association of Medical Managers) meetings enormously helpful, others felt very isolated. All were trying to maintain at least a half-time clinical practice and were feeling seriously overloaded. They were worrying about their ability to keep up to date, both clinically and with the continual changes of policy and ideas in the NHS. Many also had teaching commitments and were in demand for national committees.

A question of priorities

On their third morning with us, we invited them to consider the question of priorities. They had been developing a shared understanding of the kinds of work that the role involved and had been sharing stories about their workloads over the last two days. Now we gave them a simple form (see Figure 4.1) and asked them to complete it by listing and detailing their three most important priorities for the next year.

Priority	Why is it important?	When must it be done by?	How will you know it's done	Ideas on how to do it
1				
2				
3				

Figure 4.1 Priority analysis form

This proved almost impossible for the majority of them to tackle at first, even though the group had had an enthusiastic and participative two days. They understood that they had come to share experience, and to work together, rather than to hear what the King's Fund thought they should do. They wanted to sort their priorities and a few could, but most felt it was enormously difficult. There was a shuffling of feet and an avoidance of our eyes. Some were avoiding the task, by pretending to be studying the form, others waited for rescue and filled the time by looking through other papers.

The group is stuck

Observing that they seemed to be stuck, I asked them if any of them remembered an old children's poem about a shipwrecked sailor who, as soon as he thinks of a useful task, such as finding water or shelter, is distracted by thoughts of another, such as signalling for help, and the poem ends with him sitting on the beach completely immobilised by uncertainty. This got their attention, grins of relief and chiming in, *'That is just what was going through my head.'*

For these medical directors, no sooner would one task emerge as crucial, such as changing the culture among their consultants, than they would feel undermined by another, such as building relationships outside their trust, or leading their boards to refocus on a clinically led agenda. At the same time, there was a constant refrain of tasks that were being given to the medical directors by the chief executive and the clinical directors: all the difficult problems that had anything to do with doctors were being dumped on their laps. Any initiative, however worthy, comes to feel 'Yet another bloody thing for us to do', when medical directors are so overloaded.

Overwhelmed with tasks

Kate was the new medical director of a small acute trust – young, full of enthusiasm for her new post and keen to learn how to do well in her new role. She said,

'I am aware of so much that needs to change. My mind is buzzing with the dreadful implications of Calman for how we use junior doctors, and the shift to primary care settings is crucial to my mind. We've got to face up to the shortages in key specialties like A&E, and I can't see how we're to manage without the intensive care nurses we need. Our purchasers have not wanted to meet us but we've just got a brilliant new Director of Public Health and we mustn't miss this opportunity to change their commissioning strategy. We need to reduce the number of hospitals in our area, and that means our workloads will have to change radically. Yet none of the people I work with wants to look at such things and I haven't got time, because my days are full up with short-term maintenance work, just keeping the show on the road.'

Peter had been the medical director of his community trust for three years, a quiet older man. Peter's problem was that he was disappearing under the weight of others' expectations. He sounded depressed as well as tired:

'I am expected to attend all the medical committees and all the managerial ones, and the board, of course. Whenever there's a crisis the chief executive wants me to front the press conferences and when we have a serious complaint, she wants me to meet the relatives. I can understand her reasons, they do trust a doctor more, and I wouldn't mind doing it but there's just too much. I'm trying to keep my own six sessions going but managers expect me to be able to drop everything and go over to them whenever they have a problem with the consultants and all the clinical directors expect me to take their side whenever they are not getting what they want from the managers.'

Our initial reaction was dismay, we had got it wrong, the idea of asking for priorities was misguided. Then we recovered a bit and began to think constructively.

We decided to try offering a bit more help. Our suggestion that we had a couple of simple concepts that might assist, was greeted with enthusiastic relief. The first of these suggestions, that had been known to help other doctors, was to draw themselves a 2x2 matrix of urgency against importance (see Figure 4.2).

	Urgent	Less urgent
Very important	e.g. Filling A and E consultant and SHO vacancies	e.g. Assessing clinical risks for whole trust
Less important	e.g. Attending committees	e.g. Arranging workshops for doctors on management

Urgency vs. importance

Figure 4.2 The urgency/importance matrix

This was a particularly helpful idea for Peter. He began talking to his neighbour and then joined in the general discussion around the phrases 'taking a helicopter ride over your organisation' and 'seeing the wood for the trees' . Suddenly, the urgent and relatively unimportant priorities could be seen as obscuring the more important tasks. The doctors were then toughened in their resolve to make time for the latter. They could see that they had to decide what was important, they were being paid for just that ability to judge the clinical situation as a whole; they must not just accept managers' sense of what their priorities should be. Peter said,

> 'I think I've been a bit too accepting of the managers' view of what my role should be. When I hear some of you come out with all your ideas, I feel I am missing the boat. I've accepted a kind of dogsbody role, all the jobs that no one else wants to do and consequently I haven't had the time to think about a lot of much more important questions. I never use my office, just dump paper there. Maybe I need to make it my thinking space.'

As Harry, an experienced medical director of a large London teaching hospital, put it, *'I now see that educating the board and the managers is really a priority – I've got to get them turned round to be focused on clinical matters, with the money as secondary.'*

Some, including Kate, saw that they did not have the backup staff to help them prepare for important work and felt it was time to face managers with this reality. The others agreed that, while such action was certainly not urgent, it was actually rather important as it was limiting so much else (some did not even have the use of a secretary).

Working alone

I asked Kate if she would like the views of the rest of the group about her long list of important and not absolutely urgent priorities. They said it was an impressive list, and they were all important but one person could not hope to make much impact on them all. *'It strikes me you need to get a whole team of people working on them, what about your clinical directors or some of the managers?'*

Kate was quick to see the possibilities and said she could see how she was preventing herself from having an impact by trying to spread herself impossibly thin.

We could see that some of the group were now beginning to put a few notes on their priorities forms but the majority wanted more help. Peter said, *'Actually I think I'm worse off now. I can now see what I've been doing wrong but I don't think I am going to be able to do anything about it. My chief executive is a very persuasive woman!'*

They need to say 'No'

I gave him a few hints on 'saying no!', such as the need to get this message in early in the conversation and to keep repeating it, with sympathy but determination. I said I often tried to help people to learn how to say no, and the best way to learn seemed to be to try it out. *'Would you like to try a new way, Peter? It might help.'*

After a bit of hesitation I got him out the front, pretending he was hurrying to a clinic, with Kate playing his persuasive chief executive, catching him unawares in the corridor. They soon got into realistic dialogue and Peter hesitated and protested ineffectually, while Kate walked all over him and got him to agree to take on a whole list of tasks. I asked Kate how she had known she could get away with such unreasonable behaviour. She grinned at Peter: *'You look so easily persuaded, I just knew I could win.'* The rest of the group were able to be more helpful: they pointed out how he had tried to move away and explain he had a clinic but had let this tail away into a mumble when Kate interrupted, his low soft voice, his gentle manner, his confusion and apologetic demeanour ... They too had been quite certain that he would fail to refuse.

The submissive give-away

I added some suggestions for playing it differently: more assertive posture and voice and the firm repetition of the single word 'No' at the start of each sentence. They repeated the scene several times. At first Peter was worried, 'Don't I come over as awfully aggressive? You lot want me to lose my job!' Eventually we got a very different result, when Kate said she had felt his firmness and could not decently pursue it any further. The group said that they felt that such an approach by Peter would not be resented, although his colleagues might find it a surprising change.

Fear of seeming aggressive

The final script ran something like this:

Kate   *Ah, Peter, just the person I need. We've got a bit of a problem in learning disabilities and John [one of Peter's clinical directors] doesn't seem able to get things moving. I said I thought you'd be able to sort it out for us.*

Peter   *No. I am sorry Kate and I'll try to help you find another way round it, but I cannot take any more on at present.*

Kate   *Oh, it won't take you long and ...*

Peter   *No, sorry Kate. We do have an agreed list of my priorities you know and I am sure you would not want to jeopardise them.*

Kate   *Yes, but we all have to be flexible and this has just come up and...'*

Peter   *No, I can't do it Kate.*

Kate   *Oh, I see. All right then. I'll get onto John again. You're right to protect yourself, I should say 'No' myself more often, I'd probably get more done ...*

Now they were ready to pick their own priorities for their work as medical directors and after a few minutes of silent concentration they spent the rest of the morning discussing these with each other. Kate and Peter opted to work together, each using the other's very different approach to the medical director role as a mirror that helped them to see their own assumptions about the job.

—————————————— DISCUSSION ——————————————

This story illustrates some of the problems of time management, the avoidance of overload and making the best use of the small amounts of time that doctors can afford to devote to management. We have not yet met a group of doctors where this was not a significant issue, and offering them some simple ways of looking at the problem is seen as really helpful.

Learning to refuse low priority tasks

For some, the discovery that they could refuse what they judged to be inappropriate tasks and could do this without offending others came as a revelation. In Peter's example above, his assertiveness even prompted his 'acting' chief executive, Kate, to an unplanned bit of self-reflection about her own time management. Doctors often volunteer phrases that sum up the shift in their own attitudes in relation to time that they gain from a session focused on this problem:

> *'The important that is not urgent will always get squeezed out unless I make time for it.' 'I am a clinical leader and not a management apparatchik.' 'I don't have to accept everything that lands on my desk and I don't have to do it all today.' 'My responsibilities have bounds and it helps to define those better.' 'I need to look after myself as a resource for others'.*

It seems to help when we encourage them to see themselves as valuable resources that need care and maintenance, or rest and refreshment, if they are to maintain their value. We are no longer surprised to find doctors who believe that their own health and abilities must be ignored while there is any other demand for their services – professional training must inculcate this attitude. However, it does feel worth sowing seeds of doubt! Doctors do seem to need permission to consider their own health even when *in extremis*. A medical director told me of a colleague he had to suspend because his stress was seriously affecting the quality of his work. The consultant's response to the medical director was, *'Can you manage for me the implications that I am unable to cope? I don't want to be seen as weak.'*

While it is clear that many doctors are partly motivated by a need to be wanted and needed and liked, and some prefer to keep busy, many are also seriously overloaded. Not only does this make them unhappy and potentially unsafe, it also prevents most of them from taking much time to reflect. Consequently, old behaviours may persist long past their sell-by date and new opportunities may slip by without being noticed. Circumstances change and the worn-out doctor is caught in a 'competence trap' (see Argyris and Schön, 1996).

I hear stories of doctors who take no study leave and few holidays, have enormously high activity rates and are much relied on and appreciated by colleagues, until one day it is realised that they are out of date and then they may be pilloried by their younger peers.

Staff may suffer too: the over-busy senior doctor

- is too busy to help them or to talk properly when finally cornered;
- forgets the promises once made.

He or she may

- be so busy that they interfere without noticing what they are doing;

or

- encourage over-dependence because it is easier than helping juniors towards taking responsibility.

Finding one's priorities

Sometimes it also helps to get doctors to focus on how they wish to measure their own success in the job in a few years' time, and how others will evaluate their performance. The gradual introduction of job descriptions and managerial performance appraisals may help too. Clinical colleagues may not see the doctor when he or she is acting in their managerial role: they become invisible and are then resented for their clinical unavailability. Most said that they had taken the part-time medical director post because they wanted to affect things radically and for good and to influence top managers who do not understand clinical practice. The key phrase that seems to stick is success criteria. Few would put, 'He accepted all that I flung at him' or 'She was a very useful additional pair of hands' as their desired epitaphs. 'Making a real difference' summed up a lot of their views, which they could see meant sticking to a few priorities.

Under many of the medical directors responses to work on their priorities, as with many other doctors, is perhaps an element of the best being the enemy of the good. One question for the medical director to ponder on is whether they are on the bridge or are in charge of the engine room, whether their eyes are up surveying the surrounding sea, or down inside the noisy ship.

Another very simple idea which seems to help is that of zones of concern and zones of influence:

• within the zone of influence go such matters as one's own patients, appointment of clinical directors and board decisions;
• within the zone of concern go government policy on health care, and other issues which one cannot significantly affect.

A crucial step is to check that doctors know who the shapers and the movers are in the organisation. These are the people to approach, if one wants to influence events. They may be able to take one's concerns on directly, or they may have key information for one's own efforts.

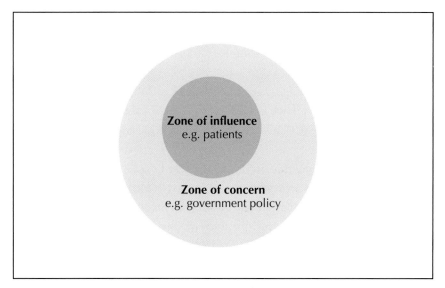

Figure 4.3 Zone of concern and zone of influence

Most doctors feel that they have an area in which they could be seriously influential, but that there is a wider area about which they are concerned. However, they feel that if they spent their energy outside their circle of influence, they might well be wasting their time. People who get obsessed with their wider zone of concern may be perceived as ineffective whingers. Fortunately, staying within the circle of one's influence tends to enlarge it, to push out its boundaries (Covey, 1992).

In managerial work, one cannot afford to accept responsibility for all the problems encountered, and doing a 'good enough' job is probably the best option (like 'good enough parenting', Winnicott, 1986) A very healthy sign we see sometimes at the end of a session at the King's Fund, are the doctors who go away saying: *'I think I will go and see my son's school play after all, he will only be Herod once.' I think I will go home at six at least three evenings a week from now on. I can see I am no longer enjoying the job and I have been letting myself get quite near burn-out.'*

These are not attitudes of accepting inadequacy but of doing one's best by behaving reasonably and looking after oneself. *'Taking time for me won't make me a poorer doctor or a poorer person.'*

Time management

In clinical work, doing one's utmost is a key value, and making mistakes is terrible. It is of the essence for doctors to want to be helpful. Gatekeeping GPs, appointment systems, waiting lists and the availability of nurses and junior doctors have served to go some way towards protecting the doctor from the stresses of managing their own time, although these are proving increasingly ineffective. They have also often meant that, medical directors' time for clinical work is to a large extent controlled by others.

We have seen a change of attitudes in the last couple of years. Previously sessions on stress management were greeted with enthusiasm and *'I'll take a set of those handouts, they would be very useful to my team.'* Now very senior doctors are recognising the need to avoid killing the goose that lays the golden eggs and they grab such material for their own use. As one said, *'I have grown too familiar with the gastro-intestinal upset at four in the morning.'* There is a recognition that too much stress narrows the range of their attention and makes them more liable to mistakes.

It may be that a doctor's essential habits for organising clinical time are not the best ones for organising management time. Sometimes it seems to help to suggest that doctors consider their own attitudes to the use of time. Many find that:

- they have a strong instinct to keep busy;
- they like being needed;
- their preference is to have a little too much to do.

When they look at possible sources for these attitudes, many find they can recall parental 'messages' that gave them this rather driven, potential workaholic base to their character. 'The devil finds work for idle hands' was the most overt. Others could remember how busy activity was praised as a child, while doing nothing, or day-dreaming, was viewed with suspicion.

The tasks that get neglected tend to be the important and difficult ones that need a good piece of time to face. Unless one puts time aside to think about these tasks, reflecting on practice or priorities, or what opportunities are coming up, they are easy to get pushed aside in the rush to complete the long list of urgent requests.

There sometimes seems to be unnecessarily submissive behaviour among medical and clinical directors, which makes me think of stories of junior doctor's hours and lack of hot food, or nurses as handmaidens putting themselves last as noble martyr figures. This is surely not appropriate for these very senior doctors? They are often the best educated and well-paid staff in their trust and they are increasingly wanting to retire early and leave for other careers. Usually, they have some control of their own activity rates, and they should be in control of how they spend their managerial efforts. Some find it difficult to arrange appropriate cover for their reduced clinical responsibilities: they feel as if they are on sufferance with their former colleagues. One said, *'I am seen as gone over to the enemy. They used to be my friends but now I have to be so careful with them and it makes me feel very alone.'*

The key messages about time management for doctors seem to be:

- in management work one must prioritise;
- it is not a weakness to need help or to refuse tasks;
- it is important and good practice to look after one's own health and energy;
- it helps to share tasks and identify key allies;
- one should be clear about one's role and responsibilities and should make them known to others.

References

Argyris C, Schön D. *Organizational Learning II: Theory, method and practice*. Reading (Mass.): Addison Wesley, 1996

Covey S. *The Seven Habits of Highly Effective Managers*. London: Simon & Schuster, 1992

Flux R, Riley J. Medical Director – What's That? *Strategic Agenda for Medical Directors*. London: King's Fund College, 1994

Winnicott D. *Home Is Where We Start from*. London: Penguin, 1986

CHAPTER 5

Who Is the Enemy?

Another common problem for doctors with managerial roles is that until recently they did not have a tradition of working collaboratively with other senior doctors across a whole organisation. Their clinical responsibilities are often relatively separate, and they have had to behave competitively with each other to secure resources for their own services. The story in this chapter dates from some years ago, yet it illustrates a problem that still persists and with which we often have to work.

This is the story of a two-day management development meeting for all the clinical directors at a district general hospital, which my colleague Andy Kennedy and I had been asked to lead.

The medical director had planned the agenda of this meeting, with the advice of the hospital's organisation development director but had then been unable to attend it. We agreed that the main aim for the day was to help the clinical directors with their management roles. They had booked a local hotel from 9am to 6pm each day. On the first day they had been joined by several of the hospital's executive directors and had had a series of lectures. The second day was planned to be for them alone, with some more input from us and time for discussion.

The nine clinical directors were all men, with varying length of service in this role. Having made the effort to get away from the hospital for two whole days (though some were going to the hospital both before and after the event with us), they were probably feeling somewhat resentful and hoping that the effort would prove worthwhile. We felt sorry that they had not been encouraged to take the whole two days away from the hospital and realised how much we had left to trust in the planning of this event.

A tension in the air

On the first day, the two of us had been struck by the tension in the room: we were unsure what was wrong, but it was clear that most of those present were unhappy and keeping at a distance. There had been several almost sullen silences, when we had asked for the clinical directors' involvement in the discussions. We had asked another colleague, who had a great deal of practical experience from her work in the USA, to lead the session on business planning. When she paused and asked them for their reactions, one of the clinical directors said it all sounded very fine when she described how business planning had been used by doctors in the States as a tool to help them achieve things they wanted to achieve, but it wouldn't work like that here. She pressed him to explore the factors that would make it so difficult here and he said, *'Well, we don't trust each other.'* There was a lot of nodding round the table from the doctors, with the managers looking more mixed: some seemed to share the view but others looked shocked.

A lack of trust

Our time was nearly up, and we both felt fairly desperate at the waste of the day and yet aware that there was now a potential breakthrough. We needed to talk this over together and replan the second day, so we called a halt and said that we would start the next morning by reviewing this day's work with the clinical directors, in order to consider whether their initial plans for the second day needed any changes.

They hardly knew each other

Andy and I then spent two hours walking and talking over what had happened. We were clear that we felt that these doctors indeed did not trust the managers in the room and were not too easy with each other – they hardly seemed to know each other. They had planned to start with a series of taught sessions the next day but pursuing these might stop us from building on some much more important material that was beginning to surface in the group. We devised a whole series of different ways to get into questions of culture and the corporacy of the group.

A culture without truth

The next morning we met the nine clinical directors and their medical director at 9am. We suggested that the issue of trust that they had raised might be very important. They seemed more relaxed this morning and several of them volunteered that it had felt very hard the day before to say anything truthful at all. We asked if this was a widespread part of the hospital's culture, and they agreed that, yes, it was.

One of us suggested that they might get more benefit by abandoning the planned programme,

'We think that you might get more out of using this relatively safe situation off-site, to get to know each other better, than from the planned topics. We think you may have some resentments about each other's priorities too and may need to talk to each other quite openly about how your various departments affect each other.'

Need to get to know each other

There was immediate enthusiasm, but then a drawing back from acting on our suggestion. We explained that there would have to be a strict confidentiality boundary round the room, and that we would only go ahead on these lines if everyone agreed it was worth a try. We got our agreement and suggested we move to the more comfortable armchairs at the other end of our meeting room. One of them volunteered to begin and we soon had a real day's work in progress, organised around a series of questions.

Sharing their worries

We asked each in turn to explain what was worrying him about the services in his directorate, as a way to get them into the management of clinical work in their own areas. They were fascinated by this and soon started an animated discussion, questioning each other and offering ideas. For example, one spoke of a scandal about to break after a suspicious death; another could not control an older consultant, whose diagnoses seemed questionable and whose colleagues would not tackle directly but brought to him for action – passing the buck. Each had several serious difficulties, and they looked relieved when colleagues showed their understanding and sympathy.

We asked them if they knew each other as people. They said that they really knew each other very little, apart from two who by chance had been at the same medical school. In turn each volunteered a quick personal history, mentioning families and hobbies. This was very simple stuff, nothing emotionally demanding, but the atmosphere was concentrated listening. I was worrying whether we were working at a deep enough level but kept telling myself to keep quiet and be patient.

We then asked them whether they might have outstanding resentments between them, as many directors do. We explained that this could be explored by asking each in turn to say what he expected of each of the other directorates and to give examples of recent interactions that had been good or bad. They jumped in with enthusiasm. By 1.30pm we were only a third of the way through. They suggested bringing the sandwiches in and we continued, talking between mouthfuls.

Exploring outstanding resentments

One spoke of the effects of his colleague's new building works on his service – how he was having to move patients on beds around the site on trolleys, across a car park in the rain, and the noise and the dust. His main complaint was that he had been refused a meeting, when he had asked to be involved in the design of the works. The others were quick to suggest alternative routes and one came up with a helpful proposal which would put his own staff to some trouble but which should help the complainant's service considerably. Before they moved on we took them back to where we had noticed the emotion – 'Was it being excluded that felt the worst bit?'

Feeling excluded

> 'Yes, yes, that was it, I was furious if I tell the truth and I think it has stayed there festering away until today. I can see why you didn't want me there but I felt so furious, so frustrated, there was nothing I could do and you didn't want to know how it was going to affect us. I thought, typical, this is how this place is and the sooner I can get out the better.'

Understanding the anger

The others were a bit stunned by this outburst but were quick to see that they would have felt the same.

The body language during this exchange had remarkably improved from the previous day – everyone leaning into the centre of the circle of chairs, smiles of understanding as well as embarrassment, people making notes. We drew attention to this and of course they could see the difference, *'The truth is hard to take but very fascinating. You cannot ignore this. This is really important stuff. We should have done this years ago.'*

Understanding others' perceptions

Two of them were now competing for the next turn, both claiming that they had had similar experiences of being excluded from planned changes that affected their directorates badly. Those who were being accused of thoughtless exclusion, were often quite shocked and defensive at first but with encouragement were able to shift into seeing what was said as perceptions, not claims to truth, and perceptions that had an understandable basis. The group was showing a lot of understanding and sympathy for each director's difficulties. There were practical responses to each situation, as it unfolded, as each was asked in turn to respond. There were offers to

Offers of help

share information, staff or equipment, to be more available for mutual discussion by keeping office doors open at certain times and eating at a particular table in the canteen. Above all, they were all agreed that they would try to say next time they were upset by each other, at the time, instead of bottling it up.

By 5.30pm all the clinical directors had cleared the air in all their relationships with each other, each conversation being more open than the last, as they experienced a growing feeling of safety in the group. It was the time we had agreed to stop but they were keen to continue: *'Now what do we do? We can't lose this. We've made so much progress today' 'We need more help, or we'll slip back into our old ways ...'*

Caricature views of managers

The doctors then discussed their views of their managers, which started off wholly as caricatures – these were surely the worst managers in the kingdom! Gradually they began to differentiate, *'Well, I suppose my business manager is*

OK really, in fact she's very good but she is exceptional.'
'And the director of personnel is all right but he is new in
from a business environment. He knows his job.' One or
two then offered that they did not actually know what the
priorities really were at the level above them. They had

Exploring managers' priorities

assumed that the board's priorities should be the same as
their own and they now saw that this was unreasonable,
'Indeed, it probably wouldn't be right if they were'.
The discussion was beginning to move into positive
waters, and we drew their attention to this but that we
were now an hour over time. We wanted to get them to
take the responsibility back from us before we closed,
so again we asked them what they were going to do
differently now, both as individuals and as a group.

Arranging another meeting

There was a rapid agreement that they would meet
again, and the first item on the agenda would be getting
the medical director's help to explore both the board's
agenda and that of all the non-executive directors. To our
pleasure, diaries were produced and a date was fixed for
another meeting. They invited us, pressed us to join them
but after a moment of silent mutual checking, we said
that we felt that they should do it alone now. We were
worried about creating a dependency on our presence,
and we were also aware that it might be difficult for them
to find our fees for further work with them.

Several weeks later, the chief executive rang on another
matter, and Andy asked him whether he had noticed any
change after the awaydays. The depressing reply was that
he didn't think he'd seen any of the clinical directors to
speak to but then he added that at the last meeting he
had got them working together at last. Perhaps he really
was a poor manager of people?

─────────────── D I S C U S S I O N ───────────────

One of the interesting points about this story is how it became clear to us all that each clinical director (CD) had drawn the boundary for his responsibilities tightly around his own service. One of our colleagues, Gordon Best, used to say it was as if the model in mind looked like a dustbin, with vertically striped sides.

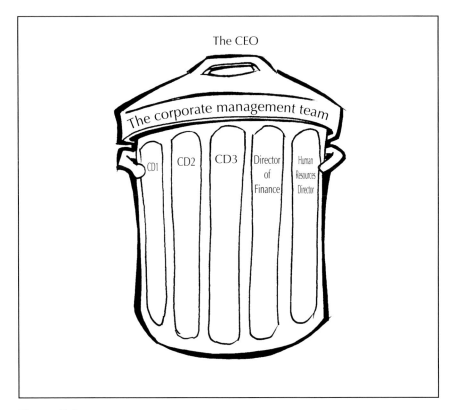

Figure 5.1

Each panel of the dustbin side represents a different professional or functional department. Individual doctors work their way up a single panel, usually staying with the same organisation once they are fully qualified. The lid of the dustbin represents those who try to work across the panels, for the organisation as a whole, with its handle being the chief executive or chair.

We often see clinical directors working alone and trying to do their best to lead their part of the hospital's clinical work and manage the staff and resources involved. Yet there is an additional more corporate way of working. When they are being corporate they are together and are focused either on helping each other with their individual directorate responsibilities, or on their joint responsibilities for the whole hospital. In this state their medical director is with them, central to this corporate role.

Their sphere of influence might be seen as extending beyond the hospital walls, certainly involving local purchasers or their services and possibly other agencies such as social services. With this wider view, some of the strength of attachment to particular buildings may be lessened, which can make easier the increasingly common mergers and the move to consider new relationships with community and primary care.

Their timescale would be longer too when working corporately, perhaps together being able to look a few years ahead.

A sense of safety

There are plenty of good reasons why senior doctors should feel it is inappropriate to share their worries or to offer help between the directorates, or similar groupings. Once they have been helped to overcome those habits, they quickly see the advantages that can be gained both in terms of practical help and emotional support from sharing more. However, such sharing is dependent on them feeling a reasonable degree of liking and respect for each other and a sense of safety, that they will not be betrayed.

One of the factors that makes trust unlikely to develop is the resentment that often builds up when people's work does affect each other, but there is little time or encouragement to communicate. Then they do not consult each other or explain why things are changing in their own areas, they do not give each other notice or ask what can be done to reduce the impact elsewhere. Each change usually has knock-on effects and it is the negative effects that are noticed and remembered and resented. The longer these resentments are left without being voiced back to their perpetrator, the more they seem to grow and form into a stereotype: 'He always gets the new equipment', 'She is the manager's favourite and can do nothing wrong.' 'He lets his team get away with murder.' Such labels then prevent co-operation. Just as clinical colleagues can readily misunderstand each other and behave as if they were trying to lead quite separate areas of work, so too managers can be excluded and resented. Improving communication between the executive and clinical directors must help.

Overcoming an accumulation of resentment is not easy without an external person who structures the process and asks for confidentiality. Do-it-yourself has obvious dangers, there has to be a private and confidential space for the expression of what may be dangerous thoughts or feelings. Making it safe enough is also a matter of the skills of facilitation: observing the different 'forces under the table' (see Chapter 2, page 15) and tuning in to all the different channels of communication (see Chapter 6, page 77). We try to model the behaviours that may help:

- flexibility;
- honesty;
- vulnerability.

It also seems to help that we prefer to operate with the complexity of real-world situations and try to avoid parroting simplistic 'solutions'.

Moving the group to a circle of informal chairs, away from the boardroom-style table had probably also helped in the story quoted. Being off-site, all together, with no normal business agenda, was crucial too: doctors are quick to understand the importance of such practical details.

The 'change equation'

We often draw doctors' attention to the idea of a 'change equation' (Beckhard and Harris, 1987):

$$C = A + B + D > X$$

Where C is change, A is the level of dissatisfaction with the status quo, B is the perceived desirability of the proposed change, D is the practicality of the change and X is the perceived 'cost' of changing.

Beckhard and Harris pointed out that change will only occur when the perceived cost of changing is less than the sum of A and B and D.

Managing in many directions

Another way of looking at this that sometimes interests doctors, is to think of oneself as at the centre of a whole set of directions for managing.

It is common for doctors, and other professionals, to think of themselves as managing 'downwards': that is, managing their staff and juniors. Some may realise, perhaps prompted by days such as the one described in the story above, that they can manage their colleagues too – in the sense of informing them, and asking and offering co-operation. Managing those outside their organisation may also be possible. Managing 'upwards', perhaps of those who control the flow of resources into their areas, can also be a useful idea.

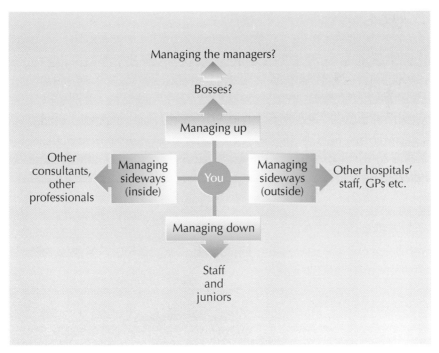

Figure 5.2 Clinical directors' directions of managing

Managing upwards usually involves making sure that staff know their boss's priorities and plans and what the boss wants and fears most from them. It also involves making sure that the boss knows what staff need from him/her, which might be feedback on performance. Other groups can be added, doctors often begin to place on their own personal diagrams their patients, referring GPs, the tertiary or community services.

I often return to this group of clinical directors in my mind, when I am feeling 'stuck' working with a group. It reminds me of the need not to let myself sink into depression when we seem to be making little progress, but rather that I must try harder to create more safety, so that some brave souls will feel able to help us escape. Yet I must also not be impatient, it does not help. Time is a curiously flexible commodity when doing this kind of work. More than half of that two-day event was 'wasted' and yet we could not have had our last few hours without that and those last few hours were really valuable.

The key messages for doctors seem to be:

- unspoken resentment builds barriers;
- honesty can break the ice, even honesty about not knowing what to do;
- change will not occur until the pain of the present situation outweighs the difficulty of making a change;
- working corporately is different from leading one area (the dustbin);
- you need to manage up and out as well as down

References

Beckhard R, Harris RT. *Organisational Transitions: Managing complex change*. 2nd edn. Reading (Mass.): Addison Wesley, 1987.

CHAPTER 6

What Lies under the Surface?

The story that follows was provided by my colleague Sholom Glouberman. It is a story with several themes. Ostensibly, it is about how Sholom worked to help a doctor/manager with the merger of two mental health units, within a northern city community services trust. The consultant involved was the clinical director of one of the units and became the director of the merged service. Sholom was engaged as her management consultant over a period of years. He attended and helped with various team meetings as well as acting as a private confidant and coach to the consultant. He did this work as part of organisation development work with her trust, which meant that he had met many of the key people in her world before he began the work which is described in this story.

F rances came to Sholom's office for their first meeting. She explained that she had taken over the clinical director role from another psychiatrist, who had pioneered the current service. Frances felt a strong loyalty to the ideas of her predecessor and to the service and so when she retired, Frances accepted the role of clinical director. Frances felt that she was primarily a clinician and had some ambivalence about assuming managerial responsibilities. She felt compelled to become the clinical director to preserve the quality of her own service. It was with similar ambivalence that she had agreed to manage the entire service after the merger. She felt that she would retain more control over the quality of the service if she managed all the services in the area.

An ambivalent clinical director

She began to talk to Sholom about her problem with Deborah, her opposite number in the eastern part of the trust. She said that her western part of the area was very well organised and delivered services to many patients. The doctors and nurses followed well-established protocols and patients were well received, well treated and properly followed up. The staff were devoted to the service and many had been there for a long time.

Her own service is high quality

By contrast, Deborah's service in the eastern part of the area seemed to her to be very poorly developed. She said it was like a club of doctors run by Deborah. The doctors were all focused on their hospital jobs, and were paid on a sessional basis for their work in the community. Most of them seemed to be friends of Deborah. Frances felt that they had little concern for their patients. Frances had been trying to give Deborah some sense of the changes needed to bring the two services up to the same standard. Deborah always agreed with whatever Frances said but never seemed to do anything about it. She also avoided meetings, pleading clinical pressure, did not reply to letters and, worst of all, she went to the personnel office and made contracts which gave all her doctors virtual tenure.

Colleague's service seen as poor quality

The community psychiatric nurse in the east had been doing the job for many years. She came from the old paternalistic (maternalistic?) days, when the nurse told you to what to do and then helped you to live with your symptoms. This was no longer the style in the west. The modern way was to advise patients (clients) about various possible treatments, present their advantages and disadvantages and then give the patient the final choice. Her method was to interview the patient, and then, using all her paramedical authority, persuade the patient to keep taking their prescribed treatment.

Frustrated by difficult people

At this meeting, Frances was plainly very upset. She spent much of the time complaining about Deborah's impossible behaviour and the nurse's rigidity. She apologised to Sholom for making him suffer through all this venom. By the end of the meeting Sholom hoped that she was relieved of some of the burden.

He made two suggestions that Frances seemed to find useful:

- the first was that maybe she envied Deborah, because Deborah could behave like a real doctor, while Frances was the doctor/manager. Sholom felt that the difference in status of mental health staff troubled Frances, but she claimed that this was only because its lower status denigrated her service;

Questions of status and authority

- the second was that he saw her as behaving towards the team in the east in the same way as the eastern nurse behaved towards her patients. Frances could be seen as having diagnosed the problem and then using all her authority to force change, without allowing the team to make their own choices. By doing this she stopped discussion and forestalled negotiation. It would improve things if she used all her clinical acumen to help the members of the other team.

Frances returned several weeks later and said that she had magically changed her relations with Deborah and the eastern management team, and felt that this was thanks to Sholom's suggestion to listen better. Sholom was not sure that he understood this change but felt he should

Importance of listening

remain silent. She said that she had begun to have weekly team meetings with the doctors, nurses and administrators and these had been going well. But now they all wanted to meet this wonderful guru who had helped Frances to do all this. So she wondered if Sholom could meet with the western team and help them with their management problems. This made him feel really good, but he wondered how he could help the western team, when it was the eastern one that was problematic. They then arranged for Sholom to attend a team meeting several weeks later. He became very nervous about this.

Sholom went to the joint meeting, arriving at the end of their business meeting. The point of his part of the meeting was to help them with the merger issues. The people at the meeting included the inner circle of the western service: the psychiatric registrar, the head community psychiatric nurse, Frances' personal assistant and the service administrator. The group from the east included Deborah, their head nurse and a senior clerk.

The meeting deteriorated very quickly into hostility between the self-assured western group and the eastern team. The two clinicians from the east were attacked mainly by the registrar. She seemed to know it all, rather loudly and

Aggression

very angrily and questioned everything Deborah said. The two nurses seemed to get along better. But Sholom's overall feeling was the registrar's attitude was making the situation much worse and that she might be more of an obstacle to the merger than Deborah. He suggested that everyone spent a bit more time listening at the meeting and suggested that people took turns listening to each other. The meeting was soon over. He felt that there had been many unexpected turns in it.

In a post-meeting review Sholom told Frances what he felt about the registrar. She agreed and began to tell him of other aspects of the registrar's somewhat troubled personal life and of her dedication to the western unit. She felt that helping the registrar to manage her burdens was part of her own job of managing. But Frances denied that the registrar was more of a problem than Deborah.

Troubled personal life

After this meeting, Frances called to say that she and the registrar had had a long talk about the relationship between the two units and that they would find ways to improve them. There had been widespread agreement that it would be useful for the entire team to have a retreat using Sholom as facilitator.

In order to prepare for the retreat, Sholom met Frances at the western unit. He wanted to see what it looked like and learn more about the organisation of the services. When he got there, what he was shown seemed extremely efficient, well maintained and well organised. The receptionist seemed friendly and responsive, the consulting rooms were well stocked and clean and the records well classified, easily located, confidential and organised in a useful way. The details of the organisation were well thought-through and Frances seemed comfortable and easy in her territory.

Well-organised services

Sholom and Frances talked through the plans for the retreat and she told him that Deborah had applied for and got another job and would leave the area. She had mixed feelings about her departure but was mostly relieved. She thought that she had handled this much desired departure quite well, by not (falsely) asking her to stay on and also expressing some concern for her reasons for leaving. She wanted to use Deborah's resignation as a chance to give the registrar most of Deborah's responsibilities and to merge the two services completely. Deborah was still invited to come to the retreat. It would be a place to talk about the future of the service, before reorganisation would take place. If they had enough time,

The process of reorganisation

they could talk through the process of reorganisation too. Sholom offered to leave the day as a chance to engage in a strategic conversation and that is where they left it.

The managerial context

They also spoke about managing the service in the context of the entire community trust and the whole area. Frances was vice-chair of a regular meeting of all the doctors in the community trust and sat as its chairperson. These doctors included the doctor/manager of a palliative care unit, a doctor/manager of women's services and the doctor/manager of a geriatric unit, whom Sholom had met before, as well as some paediatricians, whom he had never met. Together they covered a largish part of the community services and the chief executive had been asked to attend their meetings, which he had begun to do. This led Sholom to think about how these services should be organised, now that more doctors were assuming managerial roles in them.

Exploring histories and cultures

In the event, Deborah did not come to the retreat. The day had to be held, without her. Sholom says that he has learned that it is best to do some things to help at such days but more or less let them happen. Mostly, he wanted the group to try to look at their service as a whole. He noticed that everyone seemed to want to tell stories. So they spent the morning getting the history of the two services. Some of the participants had been working in them for many years. What emerged was many of the similarities and differences between the two services and ways in which they could help each other.

Sholom said that it was not good to maintain a parochial view; this service had to consider how it related to the rest of the community unit. Did it distinguish itself from other clinical services in not merely fighting for its own interests? How did it do this?

In the afternoon they worked through ways of bringing the two services together. Sholom tried to find ideas which the east could bring to the west. How would the west change because of the east?

What he now thinks is that the western service reacted to the departure of its founder by becoming quite rigid in trying to maintain her approach. The merger with the east gave it a chance to unbend and to respond to the changing world.

—————————— DISCUSSION ——————————

The overt problems in this story are very commonly brought to us by doctors: a merger to achieve, another's service is poor, and the doctor managing that service is difficult. The role of critic is an easy one and labelling another service and person does not really help much.

Sholom helped Frances to see underneath this layer and to explore her own relationship to the criticised situation and person. In his judgement, this enhanced self-awareness meant that Frances could change things in a more effective way than just take over the eastern service and disempower Deborah. Although the outcomes were the same, perhaps the process was less painful. Or maybe Frances was seen as less responsible for the changes. Having an understanding but detached confidant allowed her to share the burden of management and to feel less alone.

Multi-layered problems

We often see problems that seem to have many layers, like an onion. As a doctor is helped to see their problems, by talking them through, they will often find that there are more problems underneath. In Frances' case, underneath her worries about the quality of the eastern service, lay

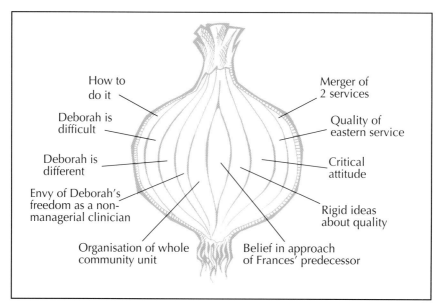

Figure 6.1 Problems layered like onions

her own critical attitude and a rigidity towards quality, that were possibly much more important to face. Under the surface problem of the merger of two differently organised services may have lain an ignoring of the wider context of the whole community unit and all its services. Under Frances' disapproval of Deborah may have lain some envy of her freedom to be more of a pure clinician. Often dislike of one person can blind one to difficulties in the behaviour of others.

One of the most important things we can often do is to show doctors how they may be part of their own problem. Sholom helped Frances to see herself inside the problem, rather than outside it; how her behaviour was not helping. We can sometimes help doctors to see this if we ask:

- How does this affect you personally?
- How could someone different from you tackle this, or see this differently?

A group of doctors can often do this for each other very well. Then the individual can become more self-aware, by watching out for such involvement in future.

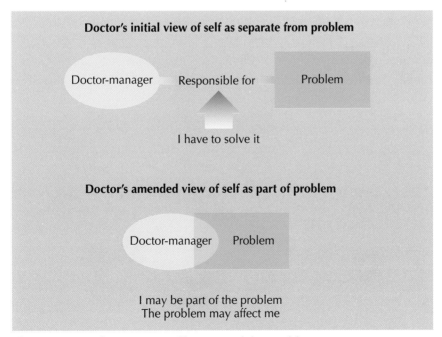

Figure 6.2 Looking at oneself as part of the problem

In this story, the situation was shifted by Deborah's move – it is worth remembering that it is always possible that something will change a situation that seems 'stuck'. Wait and see may be the best policy (see Chapter 8 on Wicked Problems).

Sholom drew attention to some of the subconscious forces at play – the history of the situation and Frances's own style and view of the boundaries of her responsibilities. These insights emerged slowly, and Frances took those that felt right to her, at her own pace. One way of looking at what Sholom did is to search for the 'forces under the surface' – he was looking for the unspoken motivations: the subconscious forces.

Subconscious forces

In Chapter 2, I used a picture of forces under a table at a meeting. Extending that idea, it can help to think of our normal perceptions of what is going on as like the little boats sailing on the lake in the top of Figure 6.3. We are unaware of what lies below us in the water: there may be hidden forces and great depths there.

We can rarely access such subconscious forces without skilled help, although it can sometimes help to ask ourselves if someone, for whom we have a strong sense of irrational liking or disliking, could be reminding us of someone else in our past. Without such insight, we may unconsciously transfer reactions that are appropriate to that past figure, or to ourselves, onto our present colleagues.

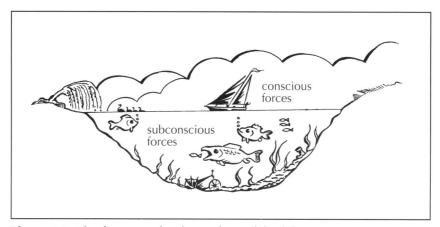

Figure 6.3 The forces under the surface of the lake

My colleague Eva Lauermann has a good technique for surfacing some of these subconscious forces, when she has a client faced with what feels like a decision they cannot take, after all the rational analysis has been done. She asks them, as an 'as if' exercise to aid their decision, to toss a coin, saying they must imagine that they accept that they will follow whatever the toss chooses. In their reaction to the toss, clients often find some previously obscured force involved in their decision. She had a doctor who had been invited by the BMA to bring his 'baby', a new professional society, under their auspices. Rational analysis insisted that this was the right thing to do, indeed logic said he must do it, yet he still felt undecided. When Eva got him to toss a coin, and it told him to take his society into the BMA, she asked him how he felt. His immediate reaction was, '*Miffed*'. Then he pondered this and realised that he felt irritated because it had not been his own initiative. Realising what had probably been blocking his decision seemed helpful. He felt he did want to take the society into the BMA. However, he took the decision to his committee. Perhaps not surprisingly, they too worked through a logical analysis of the pros and cons and concluded that it clearly pointed to acceptance of the BMA's offer but they too felt reluctant. Fortunately, he was able to break the stalemate by recounting his exercise with Eva and the committee agreed that they too had been blocked by feeling 'miffed'!

Another way of thinking about subconscious forces is to look at the difference between what have been called 'espoused theories' and 'theories in use', as explained in Chapter 2. Thus at work, Frances may have espoused a theory of managing others that included helping them with their burdens, but it did not extend to helping Deborah. Her theory in action was perhaps more one of loyalty and support to those who shared her ideas for how the service should be run.

Another of my colleagues, Huw Richards, said he describes what he is doing when working in this way as trying to watch several TV channels at once (Figure 6.4). There is so much going on, one need never be bored in a meeting again!

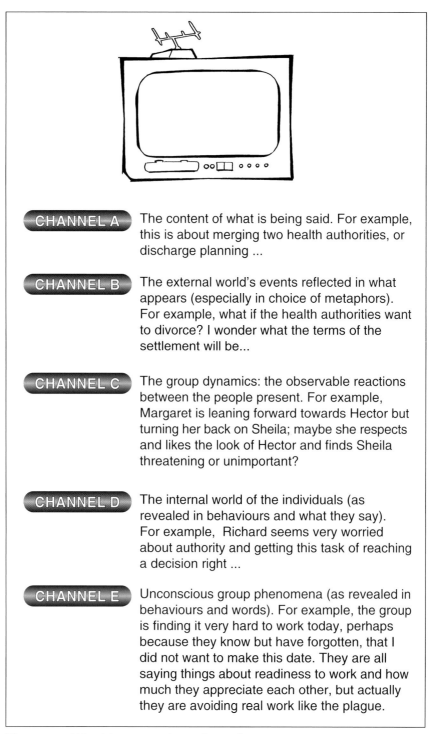

CHANNEL A The content of what is being said. For example, this is about merging two health authorities, or discharge planning ...

CHANNEL B The external world's events reflected in what appears (especially in choice of metaphors). For example, what if the health authorities want to divorce? I wonder what the terms of the settlement will be...

CHANNEL C The group dynamics: the observable reactions between the people present. For example, Margaret is leaning forward towards Hector but turning her back on Sheila; maybe she respects and likes the look of Hector and finds Sheila threatening or unimportant?

CHANNEL D The internal world of the individuals (as revealed in behaviours and what they say). For example, Richard seems very worried about authority and getting this task of reaching a decision right ...

CHANNEL E Unconscious group phenomena (as revealed in behaviours and words). For example, the group is finding it very hard to work today, perhaps because they know but have forgotten, that I did not want to make this date. They are all saying things about readiness to work and how much they appreciate each other, but actually they are avoiding real work like the plague.

Figure 6.4 Watching several TV channels at once

The key messages for doctors from this seem to be:

- problems have layers like onions;
- you are probably part of your own problem;
- there may be lots going on under the surface;
- check whether you know your theories in use as well as your espoused theories.

CHAPTER 7

Feeling Stuck

This story was given to me by my colleague Peter Mumford, who works with GPs quite often. In this case he told me of Mary, who came to him for a couple of hours of coaching on four occasions. Her difficulties were many but she might have summarised them as 'feeling stuck in a difficult situation', which she could not see how to change.

M ary was a 45-year-old GP in a busy 5-partner practice in a rural part of England. She approached Peter for some assistance with a particular problem at first, on the recommendation of another GP, with whom Peter had worked previously. Over the telephone, Mary had explained that the senior partner in her practice had been off sick for three months, and since she was the next most senior, she had taken over his responsibilities. She was feeling overwhelmed and was facing difficulties in her relationships with the other partners. There were difficulties between them too.

Feeling overwhelmed and in difficulties

Peter arranged to meet her the following week, to discuss the situation and to decide whether he could help. They met at the King's Fund, as Mary had had a meeting in London that day. After introductions and clarifying ground rules on confidentiality, Peter asked her to talk through in more depth what was going on in the practice and the circumstances that had led up to the current situation.

Mary had been with the practice for 15 years. She had joined as a full-time partner and had gone part-time 12 years previously, when she was expecting her second child. When she joined the practice, it had four partners and a reputation for being 'old-fashioned' – little had changed over the previous ten years. Mary added that the senior partner had just retired, and one more was expected to retire next year. Over the years the list size and the numbers of staff had built up along with the practice's reputation. Mary said she was the only woman partner and the only part-time GP in the practice. *'How things are fuels the sense of isolation I have. It adds stresses to the existing isolation of a rural practice, where doctors continue to be figureheads in the community. It is difficult not to feel continually on display.'*

Feeling isolated and exposed

The current partners had been together for seven years now. There had always been what Mary called, 'personality difficulties', which came to a head during the building of a new surgery and again in discussions over whether to become fundholders. They regularly surfaced over personnel issues. Over this period, Mary had found herself being handed the most difficult and contentious of these practice problems. She had been expected to sort them out with no formal authority or support, or recognition when she had been able to make progress.

Expected to handle difficult people

Peter asked her whether she saw herself as successful. Mary replied,

> 'Looking back, I can see that I have been quite successful in resolving issues for the practice. I steered through the rebuilding project. I got us second-wave fundholding. Recently, I got us into an out-of-hours co-operative. I also managed to find a job for one of the younger receptionists who couldn't cope with the pressure and was causing problems. At the time though, I often feel incompetent, that's my over-riding impression. I take longer than I think I should, I feel like an amateur and I've no idea if I'm doing it right.'

Competent but feeling incompetent

They returned to the issue mentioned over the phone. As they talked it through, it emerged that Mary felt that the senior partner was reluctant to relinquish the tiller, even though he was ill and his retirement was imminent, he was still making decisions without consulting Mary.

Mary went on to tell how she had been trying, unsuccessfully, to get the partners together to discuss the implications for the practice of the health authority's proposal to create 'localities' (to divide their staff between several local areas). The health authority had approached her to be the GP leader of their own locality.

Localities proposals

She found herself regularly working late into the evenings and over weekends on practice administration previously done by the senior partner. She felt her clinical practice was suffering and her family were beginning to resent the intrusions and having to bear the brunt of her frustration with the way things were going.

Peter offered her a summary back of what he had just heard, which she listened to carefully. Then they discussed which of the many issues raised she wanted to work on. Mary said that she could now see the immediate unsatisfactory work pressure more clearly. She had some ideas of how to hand the administrative work on to another colleague. She remained unsure how to progress the health authority issue with her colleagues, which she saw as critical for the practice and her own future.

*Sorting
priorities*

'This discussion has crystallised things for me. I've been practising for 15 years. I'm a woman, part time, it's not been an easy partnership. I've accepted an increasing load of practice management and been expected to lead on difficult people issues. I've felt overloaded but looking back I can see, surprisingly, that I have coped and achieved, where others haven't, and I've survived. Taking time out to talk it through with you has shown me this. I can begin to see the role that I have been playing and I realise that maybe I can do this. I am able. The question now is whether I keep on taking on these responsibilities. This I'd like to work on. I still struggle with confronting colleagues in conflict. It's a bit easier when I know the issue is important to the practice but most of the time it's more ambiguous than that. Unless I really explode – often with tears of anger or frustration – I usually don't get my way.'

*Getting
an overview*

Before Mary left, Peter showed her the urgent/important matrix (see page 45), hoping it might help her in future to make judgements over priorities. Peter also gave her a copy of a questionnaire about responses to conflict, suggesting she might like to try it before their next meeting. *'In the past I have seen many doctors benefit from the insight gained from relating their results to their experience and practising the alternative responses it suggests.'* They agreed to meet again about every two months, fitting the appointments in with trips that Mary had to make to London.

At their second meeting Peter asked her how she had found their first meeting. She had gone away feeling 'lighter', she said, and the matrix had proved helpful but the conflict questionnaire had seemed 'Mickey Mouse'. He suggested they began with her 'life-line' in order to see what patterns there had been which might help them look at her current situation.

'Life-line'

Mary enjoyed this, plotting out on a sheet of paper her 45 years as a gently rising line of increasing happiness and success, and providing a lively, musing commentary. The gist of it was that she had gone to medical school to meet her parents' expectations, rather than from some burning urge of her own. Her first marriage had been a disaster which ended after 18 months. She had met her present husband when she was a senior registrar, and

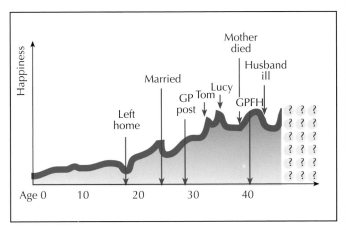

Figure 7.1 Lifeline

was pregnant when they got married. She then moved into general practice, because she needed the greater flexibility it seemed to offer, as her husband was a hospital consultant. It had not been a bad choice: her interest and commitment to general practice had grown quickly.

When she came to her present partners, her voice changed and she threw herself back in her chair. *'I can't face him, that senior partner, even though he is ill. He reminds me of my father. It's silly really, but they both have beards! I think I half expect him to slap me down for being a cheeky little girl.'*

Automatic associations

Peter encouraged her to explore the resemblance further and to list out the ways in which he was unlike her father – pointing out that this had been known to free people from some of the power of automatic associations by making them more conscious.

Peter gave her feedback again, this time pointing out her dramatic change of posture and voice, *'Your dislike of him seems really powerful, it may be coming from imaginary fears but it is having real effects on the grown-up, competent person that you are now'.*

Facing conflict

They discussed a few other ideas about facing conflict, including the need to choose her time and place for the next conversation carefully and to think how to check her posture and voice at intervals. Mary said that she expected the senior partner to be back at work next week, so this felt very timely.

Peter said he had noticed how she spoke of her career decisions as having been influenced very much by others' wishes and wondered if that was a pattern she wanted to repeat. He suggested that she might try a collage technique to surface more of her own views about her future. He left her with a pile of coloured magazines, scissors and paste, with instructions to tear out the pictures she liked on instinct, not to think about what she was doing, use her intuition, the other side of her brain, as it were.

Career planning

When he returned after about half an hour, he found she had produced a large collage and was ready to talk it through. This surfaced her desire to continue in medical practice and to take charge more. She wanted things to be organised and she wanted to be more powerful (there were power stations and pictures of muscle-builders which she said were how she felt she wanted to be). She spoke more of her fears for her family responsibilities and her guilt at what she felt was her neglect of them at present. Peter used a series of questions to get her to think it through:

- Where do you want to put effort?
- What is important to you?
- What are the underlying patterns?
- What is going to have to happen to create this desired future?

Tackling the senior partner

At their third meeting, Mary had faced her senior partner with her workload, her part-time contract and her views about continuing to carry such a load. She had been surprised by finding the conversation relatively easy and she felt he had understood her point of view. She had discovered that he had been worrying about his ability to carry an appropriate load and that he was grateful and admired her ability 'with people'. She told Peter that the most difficult thing in deciding to take less of this load, would be managing people's expectations of her, *'Mary will always step in and mop up the mess'*.

Exploring the HA localities role

She had decided to look into the localities role that had been offered to her. With Peter's help she explored her expectations about this role and what she already knew about the health authority, identifying the key areas where she needed more information. They ended with a quick look at a range of different styles of being influential.

The fourth meeting was their final one. Mary opened with her news:

Moving into the locality lead role

'I am now the GP locality lead in my area. No one really knows how it is going to go forward and I now realise that the task needs more than one person. Everyone in the health authority seems anxious for the localities thing to succeed but no-one knows what success would look like. But that is not too daunting. I don't expect to be a failure! There is far less stress and anxiety for me now, I'm much clearer about what I can bring to this role. I suppose I've begun already really. I've spent some time with the social services manager. I invited the health authority chief executive to join me at the out-of-hours co-op and she came! And I've taken up invitations to talk on the NHS changes to two, no three, different groups. I have just asked the local candidate for the Labour Party if he'd like to meet me. I think I've become more aware of the need to network and tackle the job by sharing it.'

Finding continuing support

Much of the ensuing discussion focused on how Mary could find ways of continuing to support her professional and personal development, *'Or, I fear I shall slip back into my old ways and end up a dogsbody again'.* Peter got her to identify what she felt had been crucial in helping her to see herself more clearly and to find what she wanted to do. Mary was particularly impressed by the effects of having protected time for herself to think, *'The rest of my life is all rushing about, busy, doing things'.* Peter's questions and exercises had prompted her *'to reflect afresh, to look at my behaviour relatively objectively.'* They discussed the possibilities of finding a suitable mentor, or a learning partner.

Mary ended with her thanks, *'I've really valued the chance to get away from my practice and give good attention to important areas of my professional life that I have no time for at work'.*

—————————— DISCUSSION ——————————

Time out, away from work, is often of enormous value for busy doctors to think through their options. Mary only had a total of some eight hours with Peter, fitted around her other commitments, yet it seemed to make a huge difference. Argyris and Schön (1996) use the phrase the 'reflective practitioner' to describe how professional excellence was developed. Coaching is a totally private and usually extremely efficient opportunity for that reflection, which often seems to help in the development of managerial excellence for doctors.

Opportunities for reflection

It often seems to us that many of the senior doctors that we meet are so busy doing that they have little time to think. Without a chance for review, doctors may continue in behaviours that cause a build-up of stress. As circumstances change, services must need continual review too. Coaching prompts such review by offering good attention, which in itself aids clarity. The coach may also question the doctor, in such a way that thought is provoked rather than defences raised. The use of techniques such as collage, life-lines or questionnaires do not provide answers but, as in Mary's case, give opportunities for reflection.

The coach may also give direct feedback on behaviour, noticing

- body posture;
- voice;
- what is mentioned;
- what is omitted.

It is a rare opportunity to see yourself as another sees you. Sometimes we arrange to structure this kind of feedback within a group of doctors, or doctors mixed with other professions. They may start with first impressions and go on to give feedback informally as observation develops over time. Many doctors are quite startled at first but quick to reverse their normal skills and become adept at watching themselves and others' reactions to what they do. So much of management is about managing people that understanding the effect that the doctor has on others can be extremely helpful.

Working by enabling others

Some doctors seem to find it helpful to look at the idea that one is more influential working through and with others, enabling them to share the tasks and provide allies. Whereas, much of their clinical work asks for them to work out the best course of action on their own and then try to make sure it happens. Judy Rosenor drew attention to the difference between two styles of working with staff, which she called 'transactional and transformational' (Rosenor 1990):

- *transactional management* depends on authority and control, and tasks are seen as transactions. That is, you do this in this way by this time and you will be praised; fail to do it and you will be criticised, or even disciplined.
- *transformational management*, in contrast, is more consultative, where the 'boss' sees their job as to enable others to do their work well. It assumes that most people are motivated towards good work, and if they fail it is not usually their fault.

A radiologist once described how she had had a new X-ray department built to be adjacent to a planned new casualty building. It was ten minutes' walk from the existing A&E service. During the day, staff were happy to wheel patients back and forth, but at night they preferred to use an old X-ray facility that was of poor quality but in the same block as the A&E. (They did not like the long corridors and the feeling of isolation at night.) While they complained about the quality of the machines they used at night, they were not willing to use the new facilities. After some discussion, the radiologist saw how she had been blinded by her own valuing of the new department, achieved at great effort, and her own concern for radiological quality. She had tried to impose on her staff what she had seen as an obvious solution. She realised that she had neither helped them to explore what was important to them, nor asked the A&E staff what was best for them. She was a long way from working as an enabling manager of others. Other doctors have commented, when given the idea of working by enabling others, 'I see that I don't have to control it all but it is hard to shift to trusting my staff. I realise how frightened I have been of conflict and how, because of that, I have failed to encourage my staff to voice different views from mine and so, I may have lost their ideas and their involvement.'

Mary's final meeting showed her strength in networking – an area which I think is of particular importance for doctors moving into management. Many doctors are instinctively good at this. Others find it quite difficult to build effective relationships with non-doctors:

- They ask us for help in 'managing difficult people' or 'managing multi-professional groups who are not formally under their authority'.
- They do not immediately know how to tap into the ways of influencing people that they use outside the hospital or the clinic.
- They do not understand how the other professionals see the world, or what their priorities and preferences are.
- They do not know how the other, apparently obstructive, person sees them, the doctor, and the reasons for those perceptions. they do not know what they are doing that is contributing to the difficulty between them.

Yet this is all material that most doctors can see for themselves with very little guidance. My colleague Eva Lauermann sometimes suggests that a doctor who feels in a conflict should try drawing four quick sketches (to pick up on right-brain intuition), each with a different title.

Figure 7.2 overleaf shows how a consultant sketched her clinical director, whom she found very 'difficult', as a whirlwind. In her second sketch she drew a rigid tree as herself, with her twigs being snapped off by the gales. When she explained the picture, she said, '*I am rigid, with him. I don't try to meet him halfway*'. For her third sketch, she drew a tiny mouse and a worm, as two different representations of how she saw herself, '*I'm not worth bothering with*'. Without much hesitation, her fourth sketch came out as a weeping willow, bending in the wind.

In Mary's case, the conflict with her senior partner seemed to dissolve, once Mary explained her reactions to him. One could almost say that she had been in victim mode: Karpman (1968) has suggested that we often fall into patterns of 'victim' or 'rescuer'. When one stops mentally saying, 'They won't let me' and switches into, 'This is how I could make a difference', one has escaped.

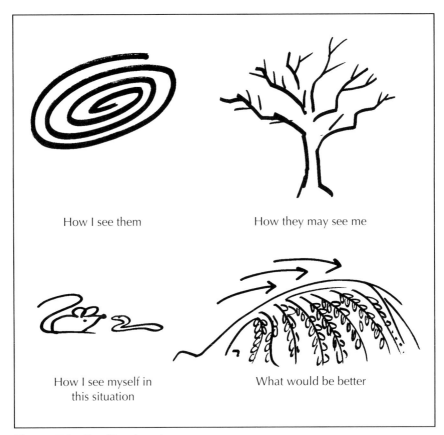

How I see them

How they may see me

How I see myself in
this situation

What would be better

Figure 7.2 Conflict drawings

Strategic management

There is often an assumption among doctors who have not had much
reflection time, that what is needed from them is administration: collecting
information, responding to documents, keeping track of resources: all lists
and files and paperwork, and deeply unattractive. While some basic record-
keeping may need doctor input, this is surely not what they should be
involved in to any great degree. We often talk of the difference between
that and managing people, making decisions and influencing others,
where doctors may appropriately be involved, often with administrative
help from business managers and secretaries and clerks.

Then the phrase '*strategic management*' often comes up, with its sense of
longer-term bigger things, providing direction to whole services. Now we
are in the arena of clinical leadership, where I most want doctors'

involvement and which may be the most creative outlet for many doctors. I do not mean only leadership of the day-to-day clinical work: setting standards and providing a figurehead, but also leading the development of ideas about how whole services should change, about clinical risk and quality. I also mean educating and influencing non-clinicians so that their debates are focused on the outcomes for patients and how these are achieved, rather than on the money, the buildings, or the staff.

The key messages for doctors seem to be:

- time out to reflect can help significantly;
- feedback alone can help, doctors need someone who plays the role of a mirror for them;
- could more of a doctor's work be done through others?
- do doctors know the views and ideas of others in their world?
- doctors are needed in management for clinical leadership, rather than administration

References

Argyris C, Schön D. *Organizational Learning II: Theory, method and practice*. Reading (Mass.): Addison Wesley, 1996

Karpman S. Fairy tales and script drama analysis. *Transactional Analysis Bulletin* No.7, April 1968, pp.39–43

Rosenor J B. Ways women lead. *Harvard Business Review* Nov–Dec 1990, pp. 119–125

CHAPTER 8

Wicked Problems

This story is about an attempt to reorganise cardiac services in the Midlands, which proved to be extremely complex. I believe that many, if not most, problems faced by managerial doctors are of this degree of complexity and they need new approaches for their effective management. The story was told to me by John McClenahan.

G erald was a specialist in cardiac medicine, widely respected for his clinical competence. He had been a consultant for four years when he joined this group of five consultants from different specialties and trusts. They met with John as their facilitator for a day, every two or three months.

Gerald had no formal managerial role, beyond that of any other consultant, but he did have a joint academic appointment and he cared passionately about the quality of the cardiac service. He could envisage a dramatic improvement of service but it was dependent on getting the three cardiology centres and the two specialist surgical units they now had in the region to combine into one. Only two of these currently shared a site. This would concentrate expertise and allow it to be much more tightly linked into academic research. Gerald was impatient, *'It's so obvious, this is what we've got to do.'*

Plan to concentrate expertise

Gradually the group questioned him and drew out that his plan had enormous implications for nearly all the staff at the five centres. They got Gerald to list these out, individual by individual, covering several sheets of flip paper, even though he was keen to minimise the list, as soon as he spotted what they were up to. Some consultants would have to change the location of their work, one would probably have to move home. Even for those who would not have to move house, they would be involved in working with a new team. Two would have to stop cardiac surgery altogether and a third needed to retire in Gerald's plan. Other members of the teams would suffer a similar range of changes.

Redundancies or moves are implied

Then the group widened their enquiries beyond the cardiac teams, 'Which other services would have to change as a result?' Services such as pathology and rehab. would have to be improved at one centre and other locations would lose some of their current work.

This would mean lab technician redundancies or moves. Gerald was looking a bit less bullish by now, he realised that his 'obvious' solution involved a very complex set of changes, many of which would be deeply unpopular to those concerned. He said that he would go away and have to do a bit more homework. He would have to 'find win-win solutions for each of them'.

The next time that the group met, Gerald was keen to secure his allocation of time. He amazed them by the work he had put in. Far from being discouraged by the cold water poured over his plan the last time, he had gone away and worked out the beginnings of an implementation plan. He described for each of the key people, his understanding of how they would be affected and what mattered to them. He had found ways to compensate several of them, by offering packages of changes.

Offering a complex implementation plan

He had, for example, secured university interest in the idea of seeking approval for a part-time academic appointment for one consultant, if he would move to the university town. He knew that this would be highly attractive to this individual. For another younger man, whose children's schooling meant he could not reasonably be expected to move, Gerald had devised the outlines of a scheme which would give him much stronger academic and senior registrar support. Gerald had two senior registrars, who wanted to build up outpatients and were excited by the idea of developing an outposted centre for cardiological investigation, and the young consultant could be offered some work in the central cardiac facility, which would give him access to an acceptable form of professional updating.

Looking at individual motivations

Members of the group now offered some more suggestions, from their experience. They did this skilfully, following John's modelling of how to introduce suggestions carefully. One said, *'Obviously, only you know what is really feasible, but I did hear that our cardiac guys were ...'* Another said, *'I don't know anything about cardiac services, but I wonder if there could be any parallels in how we persuade some of our psychiatrists to move out of the hospital and into our community trust clinics ...'* Gerald was delighted, not in the least defensive but rather, *'Well, I can't quite do that but you've given me an idea there. I could ...'* and *'That's a good idea, I could turn that on its head and ...'*

Progress and over-confidence

At the third meeting, six months had passed, and Gerald could report real progress in that the chief executive had listened to his ideas in confidence with the clinical director for surgery. They felt that they could work such a strategy into their plans and that he should leave it to them now. Gerald was full of confidence that things would move now. Almost in passing, as he ended his account, he mentioned that he had overheard the older cardiology consultant saying that he had no intention of retiring early and that the chief executive had tipped him off that the site where Gerald was thinking of centring the service was now going to be sold off. John tried to help the group to challenge Gerald's confidence but he hung on to his optimism and did not want to hear their doubts.

Unexpected changes

At the fourth meeting, Gerald reported that the clinical director had resigned and the chief executive felt that nothing should be done until the new clinical director was appointed. Gerald was torn between taking the issue back into his own hands and giving up on the managers, who he felt had let him down, or joining them by seeing if he could get the clinical director job. His inclination was to go for the latter but the group helped him, by careful questioning, to see that he did not want to give up so much clinical time (and he had a third child due).

Gerald rang John a couple of weeks after that meeting. The chief executive had just announced his own departure, and there was still no new clinical director for surgery. Gerald felt he had lost all his allies. He asked if he could talk through whether he should apply. John encouraged him to do this, just feeding him the occasional question as prompt. When Gerald rang off, John felt sure that he would apply for the two session post.

Lost all his allies

The fifth meeting was the last for which the group had funding. In the initial round of updating news, Gerald said he had not applied for the clinical director post and that he feared that he was being ostracised at work, for openly talking of the need for change in cardiac services. Two of the other members needed a lot of time for their issues and Gerald was the last to work. He looked very tired and had contributed little to the work of the group up to this point. The new baby had arrived safely but was crying a lot at night and he was getting little sleep. He explained why he had finally become sure that the clinical director post was not the right move. *'I know you were trying to get me to see all this before but somehow I couldn't see it like that then, but your wise words did sink in eventually. Or maybe it's realising that I am not quite as clever as I thought I was!'*

Changing his views

He had a sense that getting major change in the cardiac services was going to take much longer than he had thought. He wanted to talk through how he now saw it, as a means of getting himself to accept that slower pace. He began by analysing his potential allies, who now included some GP fundholders, who wanted better access for their patients and a new consultant in public health at the commissioning agency of one of their big purchasers, who seemed to know something about cardiac services. He had met Gerald at a local continuing medical education meeting, and had been at first quite critical of the services they provided. He had ended up by asking Gerald if he'd like to join their purchasing advisory

Potential allies

committee, which Gerald had indicated might suit him well.

Gerald had also begun talking to the head of pathology and, remembering the group's advice, had encouraged her to talk first about her plans. He had not realised how near they were to having a privatised service but she seemed able to cope with that and it did seem that the developments she wanted for pathology might be tied in nicely with his changes, so that very few if any laboratory staff would have to lose jobs, though several might have to change what they did and develop new specialties. *'But she thought that should be possible, that they would welcome the new work she was getting for them.'*

Not a simple problem

He said he now realised that even if he could invent ingenious 'solutions' for most of those affected, he could never make them all want the change. He had to form a network of people who cared about the quality of their services and gradually get them to believe that change was essential. The group agreed with this analysis and pointed out that by the time he had done that, local circumstances would have changed again, *'You might get a good new clinical director.', 'Maybe that older guy will retire, after all.' 'Maybe that trust will go to the wall by then, I have heard it is in trouble.'*

——————————— D I S C U S S I O N ———————————

In this story Gerald was a member of a learning set of six doctors.

Learning sets

Learning sets usually function by each member having an hour or so for their work, every time the group meets. The facilitator ensures that, during that hour, the group focuses on whoever is working and structures the discussion so that the member is able to open up his situation to the help of the other members. A firm confidentiality boundary surrounds the set, and most doctors find this way of working enormously helpful. They often gain specific advice about whatever issue they bring to the group for help. Explaining their situation to the set in itself makes them see it more clearly. Often the set members can, by their questioning, help the one who is working to see his or her own assumptions, which may be limiting their range of options. The sense of support can also be very real.

A complex situation

What Gerald was facing was a very complex situation. As it turned out, he had remarkable ability to influence: he was a natural politician, outgoing and much respected for his integrity. He was able to respond flexibly and opportunistically, so he did make some real progress towards his goal, while in that set.

Many other doctors face problems of equal complexity and are often helped by our introducing the term 'wicked problems'. This is a term from systems theory (Rittel and Webber, 1981) to describe those complex situations which by their very nature and the nature of their surrounding contexts cannot be neatly tidied up. Their four key characteristics are listed in the box below.

Wicked problems

- Wicked problems are hugely complex with interrelated parts of great complexity, so that what seems like a solution to one part of the whole, often has bad effects on another part and creates new problems elsewhere. Gerald was quick to see his proposals as sitting in a web of interconnected services and individual circumstances.

- Wicked problems are set in a sea of change, a constantly changing context, so plans become out of date as soon as they are made and consequences cannot be predicted with any accuracy. Gerald could not have predicted the departure of his clinical director, or his chief executive.

- Wicked problems have many interested parties, who do not all share a single set of values and there is no way of weighting their views. What pleases one group will probably not suit a second and will act against the interests of a third. Each of the participants in Gerald's story had their own personal career and job interests, as well as their own opinions on the future of cardiac services.

- In the NHS wicked problems usually have an emotional dimension, the pains and the gains are in terms of human lives and human suffering. What drove Gerald was not only his professional standards and the intellectual excitement of what was possible. He also lived with the knowledge of less than ideal care for patients, some of whom he knew as individuals.

This idea can give a name to doctors' experience, a justification for some of doctors' difficulties and what had previously been labelled as failure could now perhaps be seen as inevitable. They often like the idea that managing in the public sector might be more complex than in the private sector, where the emphasis on the bottom line and the removal of much of the immediate impact of politicians simplifies many problems. Even better, I am claiming that managing in health and social care is one of the most difficult forms of public sector management.

Once doctors have met this idea, they often use the term 'wicked problem' in discussing their own work.

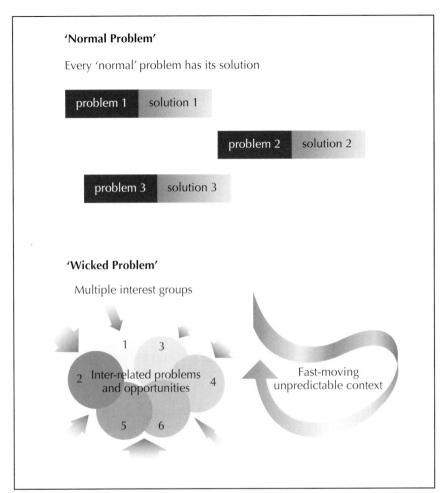

Figure 8.1 Normal and wicked problems contrasted

'If I insist on modern standards of care and try to ensure that the trust does not face an unreasonable risk of scandals, we just cannot do it with three sites. Yet the present board cannot face the politics of closing another unit. The purchasers agree in private but they say they have no more money. But it keeps me awake at night. So, you see, it is a wicked problem all right and I cannot expect a solution as such, but these are the main stakeholders and how I feel each is likely to be affected ...'

In Chapter 4, I expressed my belief that many doctors instinctively feel that they have to solve problems. I would take that further: Gerald gives us an example of a doctor who also feels he must grasp opportunities. If doctors can see how a service might be improved, they feel driven to

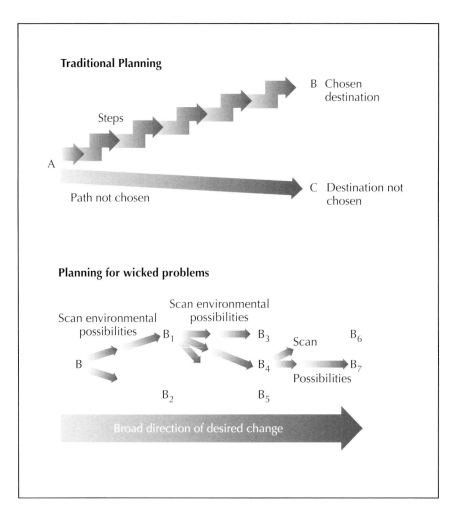

Figure 8.2 Different kinds of planning

pursue those improvements, and this has been the engine for massive good changes in the NHS. However, it is then hard for them when others do not share their priorities, or circumstances make a planned change more difficult than expected.

Some changes can be planned: with lists of tasks for the various phases of the work, each with its own deadline and maybe a chart or two. A new building or a change of clinical technique may perhaps be planned in that way. In Figure 8.2, it is as if we are at A and can imagine moving to B, by a series of steps, each of which is chosen from a number of possible alternatives.

However, in many ways, the world of health care management is often more of a world full of 'wicked problems'. Planning in the traditional way is no longer so helpful. The NHS system asks for annual plans but many become obsolete before they are finished. More flexible plans with frequent reviews, as in the second part of Figure 8.2, may be more helpful.

Another idea that can deepen debates about change, is to see four different levels of change:

1 Introducing a new task

2 Change of system or process: should we do things differently?

3 Change of purpose: should we be doing quite different things?

4 Questioning the need for the organisation or service to exist at all

As you go down the levels, you are asking more difficult questions, particularly if you allow for the loyalties and dependencies of people to existing ways of doing existing things.

One of the problems that limits all our thinking about managing the NHS may be that we are instinctively mechanistic. We have all been schooled in the ideas of what is now called 'modernism' and we think of organisations as if they were cause-and-effect equations or machines, with the various parts linked by levers. Instinctively, we cut the human beings out of our plans. It may be more helpful, if more difficult, to think in a more post-modern way, allowing for the psychological and the social, trying to see complex wholes rather than breaking things down into their constituent parts.

Perhaps we would find it more helpful to think of organisations as if they were animals rather than machines, able to adapt and survive, self-regulating, possibly even giving birth and dying.(Morgan, 1986 and Toulmin, 1990) The characteristics of living things – individuals or whole systems of animals and plants living together – are in some ways quite helpful analogies for organisations:

- living things can change when necessary, they learn and adapt when they become aware of changes around them;
- living systems are self-organising, working through shifting patterns of relationships;
- living things are experimental, innovative and rather messy and inefficient.

Thinking of an organisation as if it were in some way alive and self-regulating may reduce the felt need to control people and encourage one to work by helping them to find their own responses to difficulties.

Working with whole systems can be helpful: bringing all those concerned with a service together to share their concerns and explore the implications of their ideas (Bunker and Alban, 1992). For example, the London Health Partnership has organised many gatherings of hundreds of those who are in any way involved in the care of older people in big cities: voluntary groups, such as Help the Aged, milkmen and elderly people and carers, as well as geriatricians and GPs and district nurses. Part of their time has been devoted to mapping the complexities: for example, of all the people and movements who are involved when an older person is taken to A&E at night.

We do need to focus on developing the capacity of our organisation to make sense of changing circumstances and on developing our skills in responding to change. There is a fast-growing literature now on new ideas of how to manage wicked problems, often linked to ideas from chaos theory, that emphasise the self-generation of new patterns of organisation in turbulent environments. In this literature it is argued that we need three characteristics in our new management style:

- skills in scanning the environment to pick up changes around us that will affect us;
- emergent flexible strategies, constantly reviewed, as robust as possible;
- ways of helping staff to adapt and of using their understandings and creativity.

It is this last characteristic that may be the most difficult. Many staff find constant change extraordinarily wearing; what they want from leaders is some degree of certainty and peace to allow them to get on with their jobs. We have to find not only ways of supporting them to cope with the confusion of change, but also ways of asking more of them. We need the observations and the ideas of everyone in the organisation, if we are to help new patterns to emerge that are not imposed but genuinely self-generated.

Ways of helping staff to cope and to be creative probably lie in the following areas:

- ensuring that information flows freely at all levels;
- encouraging relationships across the usual boundaries;
- providing space to reflect on what events and trends mean and what values and assumptions are around;
- encouraging experiments and innovation;
- giving as much freedom and responsibility as possible;
- removing blocks to staff initiatives;
- getting the unspoken out, encouraging the constructive conflict of ideas.

It is as though the heart of managing for uncertainty lies in being a catalyst, rather than a planner and controller.

When we introduce ideas like this to doctors, we get mixed reactions. A few are enthusiastic, '*Now I can see why I can't do my 5-year plan, this lets me off the hook.*' or '*So what I have to do is focus more on noticing what is changing around us and less on a fixed plan, yes, I see, that's useful ...*' but often half the doctors in a group are puzzled or rejecting. Most do not hear about the underlying sense of values and gradually evolving sense of direction and they liken this approach to fire-fighting and crisis management. It feels as if we have introduced something very illogical and threatening: all their stability and ability to manage would be lost if they allowed themselves to agree with what we are suggesting.

For some, this feeling wears off quickly. As one consultant said recently, '*I realise I always react to change like I did yesterday. I find it really depressing at first, I almost have to grieve at what I am losing and I can't face what is happening to me. It usually takes about a week for me to get my mind round it.*'

For others, it remains too hard to hear and we get reactions such as,

> *'If I am going to enable my staff to help with the managing, they need some plan as a context or we'll have chaos. I can't leave it all open-ended, that would be abdicating my responsibilities.' 'You seem to be wanting to shake us up and unsettle us but all this clever talk of wicked problems and disjointed incrementalism is really just jargon and doesn't help me solve my problems.'*

Other doctors often enjoy playing with applying these ideas to their own experience. Bill, who was a clinical director in a rural district general hospital said,

> *'I see now that in this room it is the people who work in London who have found these ideas easiest to accept, have even welcomed them. I feel like an old stick-in-the-mud and I realise that I work in something of a backwater and that change is going to hit us soon. I've been seeing our trust as something that must survive and now I see that that has been an unhelpful assumption and I need to think more openly about the future.'*

Peter, who was the head of a regional blood transfusion service, came back with,

> *'It's a relief to me to know that I am not as stupid as I thought, when I cannot solve my managerial problems easily. I thought I ought to able to balance the budget and make business plans and keep all my staff happy but now I can see that it isn't that simple. I'm in a turbulent world and it's not my fault.'*

The new way of thinking is difficult but we find that most doctors enjoy the intellectual challenge of a new way of looking at their world. The challenge is to allow the paradoxes and woolly thinking in these ideas, but nonetheless see if they encourage any useful questioning of assumptions.

We have, as a faculty, to exemplify our own struggle with this very paradox in the way we design and act in our work with doctors. We often debate the degree of certainty we should give in our timetables and statements of aims. We want to provide sufficient clarity on purpose, with freedom and space to respond flexibly, to act as responsible catalysts, rather than controllers.

Some important messages in this chapter are:

- many problems are well thought of as 'wicked' and are not helped by the usual approaches to simpler problems;
- long-term plans may not always be useful or necessary;
- constant scanning for environmental change is crucial;
- management can be stimulating intellectually;
- change takes time, and people take time to change their ideas.

References

Bunker BB, Alban BT (eds.). Large group interventions. *Journal of Behavioural Science* Vol.28, No.4, 1992

Morgan G. *Images of Organisations*. London: Sage, 1986

Rittel HWJ, Webber MM. Dilemmas in a general theory of planning. In: Emery F E. *Systems Thinking* Vol.2, pp.81–102. London: Penguin, 1981

Toulmin S. *Cosmopolis: The hidden agenda of modernity*. University of Chicago Press, 1990

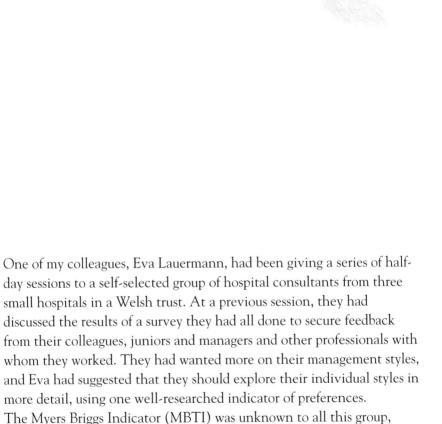

CHAPTER 9

Not Peas
in a Pod

One of my colleagues, Eva Lauermann, had been giving a series of half-day sessions to a self-selected group of hospital consultants from three small hospitals in a Welsh trust. At a previous session, they had discussed the results of a survey they had all done to secure feedback from their colleagues, juniors and managers and other professionals with whom they worked. They had wanted more on their management styles, and Eva had suggested that they should explore their individual styles in more detail, using one well-researched indicator of preferences. The Myers Briggs Indicator (MBTI) was unknown to all this group, although some doctors have now met it. I have selected this story because it seems to shed some light on an area that many doctors find difficult: working with other people, especially people who react differently from them.

Eva began by explaining that the Myers Briggs Indicator is a tool that identifies people's preferred ways of working. She started by telling them about British Airways pilots as an analogy with their work, as she used to work there. The majority of pilots are of one type, according to Myers Briggs. 85 per cent of them are what is known as STJ types – very systematic and logical – whereas this type is only shown among 15 per cent of the population. The risk with STJs is that they can get overloaded with information and if too many things go wrong, they can get fixed on one piece of data, unable to see other indicators.

For example, in the crash approaching Birmingham airport, the pilots decided that the wrong engine was on fire and switched it off. Many doctors may also suffer from this problem. You don't need two pilots to fly a plane but you do need a second person to challenge the thinking of the first. Ideally, there should be other types in the cockpit, who are more likely to be able to take a broad overview of a situation and keep a variety of options open in their minds. Eva pointed out that it had surprised her, coming to work with the NHS, to discover that doctors do not automatically have a second opinion system and did not willingly put themselves through frequent checks on their performance. Pilots willingly accept a performance culture and six-monthly checks.

She then explained what the MBTI is and what it is not. In particular, she stressed that it is a type indicator, not measuring traits and not a test. It sorts people into 16 boxes, each of which is of a different type. This took some time to establish, as the group were more familiar with questionnaires based on trait theories, which sort people around some assumed normal score, with an assumption that if they score at the extremes, they are in some way abnormal. There were lots of questions, and Eva had to assure them again that the Indicator was not a test, in that it was easy to falsify their answers if they

Every type is valuable

wanted to and there are no right or wrong answers. She pointed out the title of the original book, *Gifts Differing*, (which describes the decades of research that went into forming the Indicator): every personality type has its own gifts. This seemed to reassure the doctors, so used to exam-type tests with the notion of pass or fail.

One of the group said he *'had problems with whether she was saying that this was the only theory of personality'*, and quoted about five different models at her. Eva hastily reassured him that this was not her claim, but that this particular indicator was a way of providing the group with a vocabulary for discussing and some greater understanding of differences such that it could be a working tool for them.

The group completed questionnaires

Without explaining any more about the instrument, she invited them to complete the questionnaire. *'Should this be in work or home mode?'* Eva pointed out that, if they did indeed feel that they were very different at home and at work, this should perhaps consider what forced these differences and whether it mattered to them. However, she went on to suggest that 'shoes off' mode would probably be the most helpful. Eva promised that the profiles which scoring would reveal would not be disclosed to their organisation but it would help if everyone felt they could give their permission now for making these public in this group. There were nods of assent all round.

As she watched them, she saw that two doctors were reading it all the way through very closely, while others were talking to neighbours as they went. Some had found the suggested pencil, others ignored this instruction and used the pen they had to hand. After a few minutes, two were looking worried, *'I can't answer, it all depends ...'*, and she encouraged them to reread what the instructions said about this dilemma.

Experiential learning about types

After about 20 minutes, some had finished. Others took much longer, and this posed a bit of a problem, as people became aware that others were quicker or slower than they were. Eva pointed out that the questionnaires were designed by a particular type and therefore suited certain types better than others. One doctor said he kept thinking, *'It all depends'*, but they all laughed when Eva pointed out that this too was probably indicative of his type.

Eventually, when everyone had finished, Eva explained that now the questionnaires were done, she could explain more of the ideas behind the instrument. She explained that the types came from four dichotomies developed by Myers and Briggs based on Jung's personality work.

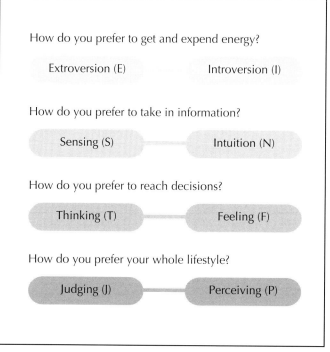

How do you prefer to get and expend energy?

Extroversion (E)   Introversion (I)

How do you prefer to take in information?

Sensing (S) —— Intuition (N)

How do you prefer to reach decisions?

Thinking (T) —— Feeling (F)

How do you prefer your whole lifestyle?

Judging (J) —— Perceiving (P)

Figure 9.1 MBT1 – The four dichotomies of preferences

Preferences in getting and expending energy

The first dichotomy distinguishes between 'extroverts' (E) – those people who prefer to get and expend energy on the outer world of people, activities, etc. – and 'introverts' (I) – those of us who inhabit the inner world of ideas and reflection. Eva explained that, unfortunately, as these terms have come to have very different meanings in the vernacular, she would have to ask the group to listen very carefully to the original definitions as used for this indicator.

Preferences in taking in information

The second dichotomy distinguishes the ways in which people prefer to take in information from the world: what is called the 'perceiving function'. Either people prefer to use sensing (S): the five senses, focusing on details, remembering sensations and operating effectively in the here and now; or they prefer to look at the bigger picture and focus on patterns and possibilities and concepts, which is known as intuition (N). Eva illustrated this concept by asking the consultants to imagine they were going on a train journey through very beautiful scenery. Those who preferred to take in information in the N type might well miss much of the experience, if they were worrying about a difficult meeting at their destination.

Preferences in reaching decisions

The third dichotomy is called the 'judging function' and identifies how people prefer to reach decisions: either through focusing on objective facts (T), the thinkers; or by paying attention to those involved in the decision and their feelings and values (F). Before she could complete the explanation, someone shot out with, *'Does that mean the thinkers have no feelings or integrity?'* Eva reassured them, that once again, the titles were perhaps unhelpful and stressed that it was a matter of preferences for making decisions: it did not mean that the thinkers had no emotions or did not care for others' views, but they would prefer to incorporate these into their decisions in the form of objective facts.

The final dichotomy looks at preferences in overall lifestyle. Eva explained that the judging (J) type preferred

Preferences in overall lifestyle

to lead an ordered, planned, decisive life in the outer world, whereas the perceivers (P) preferred to run their lives in a more playful open-ended way.

Before she could ask them to do it, everyone was placing themselves on the four lines, *'I'm more of a J, I think, and definitely an E ...'* Eva added that the theory said individual people would have a definite preference for one or the other in each pair of letters and the questionnaire was designed to help reveal these preferences but they should only use it as a guide; their own instincts as to their types were also important. If they felt uncertain, that was OK too. The distance along the line was purely a matter of degree of certainty about one's preference. They were very noisy at this point, full of talk, *'We must all be extroverts'.*

Identifying their individual types

When they had all placed themselves on the four lines, Eva helped them to score their questionnaires. It turned out that for most people, the two results coincided: their questionnaire responses backed up their own guesses from their initial understanding of the categories. Much relief for Eva. Two had very different outcomes and were perplexed. A third said that she felt it was fundamentally flawed but she was willing to suspend disbelief a bit longer.

Eva stressed again that whatever set of letters they felt was right, was right for them, the questionnaire was only an extra check, it was not infallible. The results were not about putting a person in a box, saying this is how you are and how you will be for ever more. She gave them a booklet with gave a more detailed description of the 16 different combinations of letters. There were many laughs and murmurs of recognition as people saw descriptions that they recognised as typical of themselves. There were people comparing notes, *'This really explains why I have trouble providing all the detail people seem to need of me.'* Eva stressed that the descriptions might provide an explanation for preferences, but they should not be used as an excuse.

Others said, *'This is a lot like a horoscope, I can't believe someone researched this for years!'* Others were still looking unsure, and the two whose questionnaire results were different from their own guesses were still very perplexed. *'I can fit several of these type descriptions.'* Eva urged them to hold off from deciding while the group did some further work to make the categories more real by looking at 'type dynamics' – the ways in which separate parts of the profiles interact.

Doubts and difficulties

Eva put up an empty four by four matrix, each box containing a different set of the letters and invited those who were fairly sure of their type to put their names up, if they felt happy to do so. *'Then we can see what types we have in the group'.* Most hurried to comply and there was a buzz of comments and questions. *'Are all groups like this, with a similar spread?'* (Yes, it's common). *'Did different clinical specialties have different profiles?'* (Yes and there are some data). One who found himself alone in his box said, *'I now understand why I am so different from my colleagues and so often feel the odd one out.'*

The group expressed surprise that over a third of them had a preference for introversion, even though they had been so loudly talkative. Eva drew their attention to this, *'A few Es go a long way! Extroverts need to think out loud, often if I ask a group to "think" about something, the Es immediately start talking to each other. You don't see the Is. What often happens at work is that the introverts are not heard, or you Es experience them as boring.'*

Introverts often seem invisible

Immediately the radiologist (an I), said, *'That's it exactly, I can't get a word in edgeways, I often feel invisible at meetings.'* One of the surgeons (an ESTJ) confessed that he was realising that those he ignored were usually the ones who were questioning the purpose, *'We run ahead, we get it all sewn up, we jump for the first solution we think of and we may often be addressing the wrong issue entirely.'* Another surgeon added, *'The organisation is so J it's very hard to be a P and hold options open.'*

Preferences in learning

Eva suggested that E and I types would have different preferences in how they learned. The Is enjoy reading and going away to reflect, the Es prefer to think out loud and learn best by discussing things. There was an immediate recognition of these preferences in the group and one of the extroverts said, *'Now I understand why I never read my papers before meetings!'* And I chimed in, *'And now I see why I always want to delay a decision and not take it in a meeting. I need to do some reading round it and have time to think in peace.'*

Preferences under stress

The theory suggests that one of the letters is dominant most of the time but Eva pointed out that under stress, one can get into the grip of the opposite of one's dominant preference, which is called 'the inferior'. Because it is ill formed and a childlike state, it comes out in rather extreme and undeveloped ways. She invited the group to move and sit with at least one other person with a similar profile and then explore the inferior by discussing, *'What are you like at your worst?'* Much laughter and mock shame as people recounted their least helpful moments and remembered some of the criticisms in the feedback they had got from their survey of their colleagues.

Understanding differences

She gave them a few other questions to try, *'What would people describe as your greatest quality, on first acquaintance and later? What kinds of people irritate you most? What constitutes the best kind of reward for you? What gives you joy?'* After about 20 minutes she suggested they changed round and sat with one or more people who shared as few of their preferences as possible and ran through her questions again. A final plenary discussion ended the session. One consultant said, *'I feel so much better. I used to feel bad because I did not seem to want to be the same as everyone else. Now I can see why certain people annoy me and why they find me peculiar. We just like doing things differently.'*

———————————————— DISCUSSION ————————————————

Doctors report many difficulties with working with other people, as do managers and other professionals. This story illustrates one strand of potential difficulties – people do not realise that they are different. We would argue that diversity is a good thing in itself: it is interesting and far more talents are needed than can be contained in a single type of person. Teams are not just together to bring their different responsibilities together, they can usually do more than that, especially if they can bring their different abilities into play together. Those who are strong on data need others who take more of an overview or who are more interested in ideas and vice versa.

However, difference can also be irritating and lead to painful misunderstandings. Some of the cases which doctors have labelled as 'difficult' people, sometimes seem to be little more than people who work in a different way from themselves. They were seeing how each type needed the input from other types but could easily misunderstand their reactions: the Ps hated the Js' decisiveness but they needed the Js when there was a deadline; the Js could find the Ps too airy-fairy but they needed them to stay with possibilities and not close down the options too quickly.

There are many ways of bringing these differences of style, skills, interests, etc., out into the open, the MBTI is just one. In our experience, once the differences of individual team members are made overt by some such device being used amongst team members, they are much more likely to be able to capitalise on their diversity and cope with their differences. MBTI seems particularly useful, as it provides a way into discussing differences of style and of preferred ways of working and it is not open to much criticism on the grounds of its validity or reliability, although its terminology is a real problem at first.

Other management questionnaires have also been found useful, but only when doctors were willing to try them as prompts to thought, rather than as research instruments. For example, we sometimes offer doctors Belbin's ideas about the need for a team to have nine different roles played (Belbin, 1993):

The specialist – who brings technical knowledge that is in short supply

The teamworker – who supports other members

The implementer – who is the practical organiser

The co-ordinator – who clarifies and promotes decision-making

The shaper – who drives and challenges

The plant – creative and unorthodox

The monitor-evaluator – who analyses others' work

The resource-investigator – who brings in new contacts and ideas from elsewhere

The completer – who worries about deadlines and checks details

Belbin developed a questionnaire that allows people to check which roles they most commonly play and prompts them to think whether there are any of the nine roles missing in their own working groups. If any are missing, this does not mean necessarily that the team must be expanded in numbers. It may be that some existing member could play more roles, if encouraged to do this, or some procedures put in place to cover for the missing role. For example, if there is no completer in the group, there could be an agreement to check progress at the start of each meeting.

Doctors often ask us what the best style is for a manager. Irritatingly, I would always answer that there is no one optimum. There are books on leadership or management which offer lists of desirable characteristics, such as clarity of vision or a liking for people, but these do not seem much use to doctors (or managers), and there is little evidence for their being causally linked to success even in the commercial world.

Style comes from a combination of one's innate preferences, modified by how one was brought up and the opportunities that life has offered to develop, plus the socialisation of one's professional training. In becoming part-time managers, doctors may want to consider whether absolutely all aspects of their clinical style are appropriate in their new role. It may be, for example, that a little more openness and use of their emotions may be helpful. It may be that they do not need to rush into activity on every task that comes their way. It may be that encouraging others and listening to them, more than comes naturally, would be a good idea. It may also be that some of the changes they experience as managers, some forms of personal development, may allow some unwanted habits, carried from childhood, to drop away. For example, being clever and being able to see the flaws in some proposal or piece of work, may not always be the wisest behaviour to display!

A 'whole' person

Above all, what is wanted as a managerial style is a whole person, a whole human being, uncertainties and all, and not perhaps as much 'putting on an act' as doctors believe they have to do to survive their day-to-day clinical work. I suggest that doctors ask themselves whether they are different personalities at home from how they are at work. Some who have relaxed a little into a managerial style that feels authentically their own, and stopped striving for some ideal they had in mind (often rather tough and decisive), tell us that this felt considerably less stressful.

Another way of looking at managerial style is to use this diagram based on what is known as the Johari window. (The unusual name is derived from the first names of its two originators: Joseph Luft and Harry Ingham (Luft, 1966).) It can be seen as helpful to be able to relax the boundaries

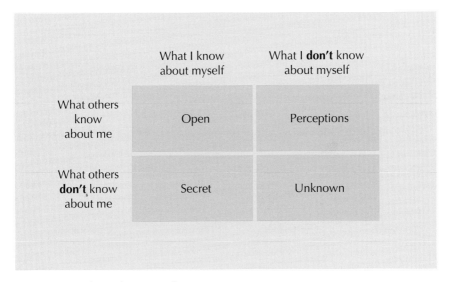

Figure 9.2 The Johari window

of the top left-hand box, showing more of the individual's real self to the world and letting others give them feedback on how they see that person at work.

The key messages for doctors seem to be:

- people prefer to work in different ways
- perceiving someone as different does not mean they are necessarily also difficult!
- there is no best style for managing
- it helps to give people the freedom to work in the way that best suits them
- it is less stressful if you can reduce any gap between your home self and your work self

References

Belbin RM. *Team Roles at Work.* Butterworth-Heinemann, 1993

Briggs, I Myers with Myers PB. *Gifts Differing: Understanding personality type.* Palo Alto (CA): Consulting Psychologists Press, 1993

Luft H. *Group Process: An introduction to group dynamics.* Palo Alto (CA): The National Press, 1966

CHAPTER 10

Adult
Friends

This is the story of Jane, a consultant anaesthetist, who needed help
with a new role: clinical services manager for theatres. She used our help
in a range of different forms over a period of years and built quite a close
relationship with one of our faculty, John McClenahan, who told me her
story.

Deciding
to take a
management
role

W
e first met Jane when she came on a week-long 'Management for Consultants' programme about 5 years ago. She had been prompted to get some management training by the request to her to take on the management of the theatres where she worked, an unusual role for a doctor. During the course, she had the chance of a session in a small group, or development set, focused on her current situation. She chose to explore this new role. *'What do I really feel about doing it? I am not absolutely sure whether to accept it. How can I make it a do-able job? Who do I need to work with?'* She found the ensuing discussion with five doctors from different backgrounds useful, she said. *'Talking to others helps. I realise that there are one or two key bits of information I need before deciding.'* Later we heard that she had accepted the management post, with a 20 per cent reduction in her anaesthetic sessions.

Failing to
manage the
budget

Eight of the consultants on the programme came to the two follow-up days at the King's Fund at six monthly intervals, after the course was over. Jane came to both of these. Once again, there was time for her to raise her issues in a small mixed specialty group, and with these by now familiar faces, she chose to explore a very difficult area. She was deeply concerned that their activity levels were rising fast, yet their allocated budget was not rising fast enough to keep pace and theatres had a reputation for being chronically over-budget. She knew that her chief executive was angry and felt she was being labelled as a failure as a doctor-manager. She struggled to say, *'And that is very hurtful'*, feeling near to tears with it. The group saw Jane as someone who was very competent clinically and who had a strong sense of integrity. They also knew that she lived alone and had little or no emotional support at work and was working extremely long hours. She did not normally show much emotion and had not told them that she was feeling unwell these days, which she self-diagnosed as stress-induced.

One of the group, a physician, who had been a clinical director for some years, said, quite forcefully, *'Jane, I know you're a good egg and its not your fault but, if I was him and all I knew was those bare figures, I think I would feel just the same as he seems to. How can he trust you? I'd be dead worried about either your competence or your commitment.'* This challenged Jane's assumption that she was the victim. She allowed that she had avoided all face-to-face contact with the chief executive and did her best to hide the situation. She remembered that she had been too busy in her own mind to seek him out and had failed to attend the meetings he had suggested. Gradually she shifted to a position where she was working on,

Trying to hide the failure

> *'How can I manage his impression of me?', which felt much more positive and cheerfully active. She found that she could imagine what he thought of her and could see what would help her chief executive to understand her position better. 'If I meet him when I'm feeling like I was, all het up and defensive, it won't help ...'*

The need to talk more openly

Then the group asked her about other key players in managing her theatres and she described her relationship with her anaesthetic colleagues, the surgeons and some of the ODAs and nurses. Before they pointed it out, she got there, *'I don't talk to any of them enough, do I? I can see that now. Maybe I should share these figures more widely, after all they are the ones who are more in control of the causes of the rising activity levels.'*

She was ready to sign off and thank them for helping her but John asked the group if there was anything they wanted to add, before they moved on to another person. Several chimed in with, *'You're having a pretty tough time.', 'I think Jane , you are expecting an awful lot of yourself.' 'I am glad I am not having to cope with all that, I don't know I'd be surviving as well as you seem to be doing.'* This shower of empathy was very powerful, particularly as some of the remarks came from doctors

Other doctors understand

whom Jane knew to be coping well with extremely heavy workloads and complex lives. One of them, who was a single mother, later worked on her own problem, during which it became clear how she organised her work into a 40 hour week. Jane commented at the end of her session, *'I can see this is not easy but you do it by being very clear about what needs you to do it and what could be done by someone else, even if not as well. I think there might be a very important lesson for me in there.'*

The importance of priorities

A year later she rang John for a telephone review of her progress in the job. This showed things to be going well, although her budget was still insufficient for all the work that was booked, she did feel that the clinical director was getting this sorted on her behalf with the chief executive. She mainly wanted to run through her reactions to her relationship with a neighbouring trust. Both hospitals were struggling financially. They shared some cross-cover, but Jane worried that this co-operation might break down under the pressures to behave competitively. John asked her about her purchasers' views and she realised that she did not know their intentions. She rang off, saying she felt pleased by having had the chance to talk to someone, *'I feel clearer just having said it to you and I can see that this is a serious situation, not just something I've blown up out of proportion. And I can see how to start to do something to improve the situation. I feel much better now and ready to get on with things. Thank you very much.'*

Relationships between trusts and her purchasers

A few months later, John was designing a new modular workshop potentially of relevance to her work. He rang Jane, among others, for her advice. In the course of that conversation, she asked him to visit her at work, at her expense, to give her some advice, particularly about her theatre supervisor, Hugh. She respected him clinically but said they were always arguing over what he was responsible for. *'Sometimes he seems not to want to do all his job and sometimes I think he wants to take me over!'* John went and spent half a day, meeting Hugh the

Arguments with the theatre supervisor

theatre supervisor, two other doctors and a key nurse and had a tour of the extensive facilities. John discussed Jane's problem with her afterwards at some length, emphasising that Hugh seemed to think he was very busy, managing the theatre nurses' contribution and that he was finding Jane difficult. John wondered if Jane was taking Hugh rather too much for granted and letting him feel more criticised than appreciated. They left it that Jane would discuss Hugh's role with him. Jane said she felt much better now that John had seen her situation and met Hugh. John pointed out that he had listened to her and wondered if she had enough people to share problems with, but Jane did not want to pursue this thought at this time. John reminded her of her interest in the last mixed group of doctors she had attended, in the woman doctor who had kept her workload down to 40 hours a week. *'Do you think you may assume 100 per cent commitment from others, who may perhaps not have told you of their commitments at home?'* Jane took the point.

Taking him for granted

When the new workshop was offered, Jane came to the first one, with one of the surgeons she worked with. The programme included working on current real problems using forcefield and stakeholder analysis (see pages 31 and 32).

Jane and her surgeon colleague at the workshop went on to a mutually agreed set of success criteria for theatre management, which Jane was subsequently to find extremely useful. Then they worked together for three hours in a little huddle in a corner of the coffee lounge. It emerged that this was prompted by a chance remark about Jane's responsibilities from the surgeon. They soon realised that they had never really sorted out their mutual responsibilities and where the boundaries between them lay. There was a lot of, *'But I thought you were doing that ...'* and *'Do you mean to say, you thought I was responsible for that. I don't think anyone is doing that...'* At the end of the day they reported back that it had been hugely useful to have had this space away together, to get

Sorting out responsibilities with the surgeons

to grips with their differences of perception and that they had sorted a lot of misunderstandings. They both felt pleased with this piece of work and had high hopes of working better together in the future.

A team from another hospital told the workshop participants about introducing a large expansion of day surgery. They had had a big block from problems with the porters at first. Then someone had noticed that in a survey of patients' views of experiencing surgery, there had been a point made about how much one patient had disliked lying on his back on a trolley, feeling groggy and being wheeled about with only a view of the ceiling, *'Quite disorienting.'* They had then asked the day surgery patients and most had said they would much prefer to be allowed to walk into the theatre and lie down when they had had a glance round. Jane and her surgeon colleague looked at each other with big smiles – *'Wow, that challenges our assumptions. We will certainly want to think that through for our situation. That could be very helpful.'*

Should patients walk into theatre?

The next day, Jane told John over lunch that Hugh was leaving. John asked her if she had a good job description to help her think how to replace him and learned that she had never had that talk to sort out his responsibilities. When Jane came to the second module of the workshop, she confessed that she had had to replace Hugh with two people. She had discovered how much Hugh had done that she had never known about. She did some work on defining the roles for these two new posts but also came to see some of the patterns in her own behaviour. She said,

Failing to praise and to communicate

> *'I shall have to watch that I don't take them for granted, as I did Hugh. I don't want them to leave me because I don't appreciate them properly! I know I will be tempted not to sort this out, I tend to assume that others share my understanding of what needs to be done and don't have their own priorities'.*

She added, *'I have been talking more to the chief executive these last few months and its been much better. I feel he understands my position and is not blaming me so much.'*

DISCUSSION

What strikes me initially about this story is how much Jane benefited from sharing her difficulties with others who had no particular axe to grind. Perhaps Jane was more alone than most doctors but her keeping her difficulties to herself is something we have seen many times before. Managerial doctors rarely meet others whom they feel they can talk to freely. They meet colleagues for clinical conversations obviously, but there is usually an assumption either that other doctors at work will not be interested in management, or that there may be some disadvantage in sharing. Perhaps this is based in legitimate concerns about competition, or maybe it stems from a feeling that management is not something proper doctors do: one has 'gone over to the enemy'. Being listened to with full attention for half an hour or more is in itself unusual. Being aware of that attention, one becomes more able to hear oneself. One can gain from the release of having poured it all out and one can double back on oneself and see how one sounds, how one has been feeling, how one has been viewing the problem.

'Is it me, or is it them, or is it the situation?'

One of the things that Jane wanted to know was whether her reactions to events were reasonable. *'Is it me, or is it them, or is it the situation?'* Unable to see themselves clearly, doctors find it hard to sort this out on their own. They feel they lack standards of comparison and the fear of being a failure is there for most doctors: *'How well am I doing?'*

The group were also able to use their different reactions to her issue and their different experiences of management, to imagine a variety of different ways of reading her account and reacting to her situation. It is common in such development sets (Riley, 1995 and McGill and Beaty, 1995) for different views to be expressed. This often enables doctors to see the box within which they constrain their actions: the set of assumptions which limit their search for solutions to their difficulties. They were also able to help her find for herself, or see the need to get information on, other key stakeholders' reactions and to understand these alternative views. The facilitator has to make the group safe as a container for difficult work and to enable serious challenges to be made constructively and to be heard and used the part of those who are criticised. In the story of Jane, I see her peers as able to move beyond the 'comfort zone' of normal social supportive chat, into truly helpful challenging.

Members also claim that they learn from each others' difficulties, not just from the attention to their own issue in their time slot. They talk of the value of such groups in terms of, '*It was really useful just to know that others felt the same and had the same kind of difficulties. I hadn't expected that.*' '*I didn't realise that people from other specialties from my own could be so useful but its the difference and them having no axe to grind that is so helpful.*'

Many also come to value these people as new friends and ring each other up about all sorts of things and arrange to meet socially. I know I made many of the friends that I have now in my fifties when I was at school, or in my early 20s. To make new friends as a mature adult is rare and can be very precious, particularly to senior doctors who may feel isolated at work.

A good listener

I see Jane's story as also showing the value of having a flexible detached outsider – in her case, John. Jane was able to access a series of different forms of development of her abilities as a manager, as the need arose, when her motivation to learn was ready, and in a form that suited her circumstances. Being able to secure a good listener who understands your situation, down the telephone, seems hugely helpful for the occasional urgent crisis. Getting someone to visit, when it suits your need can also be far more useful than any pre-planned 'development opportunity'.

John was genuinely interested in Jane's difficulties but had no desire to impose his own views or give her advice. He could tell her what he perceived to be the situation. This may have been particularly helpful to Jane, who for all her obvious intelligence and commitment, was not good at guessing what others might be thinking.

We often meet doctors who make a logical case for something, entirely from the point of view of their own specialty, and expect that to be sufficient to achieve their desired change. They fail to realise that others have other concerns and backgrounds and may neither understand the force of their case, nor share the doctor's assessment of its merits. Often a case to managers may need more information. John told me of another example, where cancer services were consistently starved of resources by management decisions. When cancer centres were mooted, the managers were horrified to discover that their services were not of sufficient quality to be considered. They were not stupid but they did not have the experience or insider knowledge to have foreseen the implications of their earlier decisions. They needed it spelling out: no money for new equipment will mean we become less attractive to the best doctors as a place to work, and then our reputation will fall with the best nurses and other staff and ECRs will not come our way, and gradually our services will become second rate or worse.

In Chapter 5, I included a figure suggesting that one could manage in various directions. There is a phrase, 'managing up' (Gabarro and Kotter, 1993). Doctors need to learn to think of managing those who make key decisions that affect their services. To do this, doctors need to understand those who wield this power, what their priorities are and the state of their understanding of the doctors' situations and their views of those problems.

One way of looking at it, is to say to oneself that making the logical case is step 1, and that comes from my own position. I then have to jump over into the manager's position and perceive his perspective, as step 2. Step 3 is to modify my case, so that it is translated into a form that will slot into the manager's perception as I want it to and not be relegated to an old

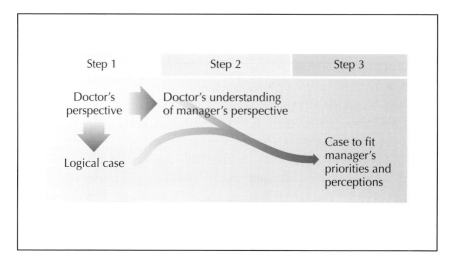

Figure 10.1 Three steps in making a case

waste bin marked, 'shroud waving' or 'greedy doctors'. Three steps are required to make a case effectively and intelligently, and it is no good stopping at step 1 and then complaining when one's request is rejected. For a step 1 presentation is almost bound to be misunderstood and not seen in its proper context.

Doctors and managers may also differ in the sources of information that they respect. Both may take well-run research trials seriously but in addition, doctors may often try a new practice if it is provoked by patients' reactions, while managers may be more influenced by 'bench-marking'; that is, by hearing of what another trust is doing. So, In Jane's case, an account of patients' reactions to portered trolleys was telling because it came from patients themselves. A manager might be more strongly influenced if it was said to be the best practice, or what the theatres with the most innovative reputations are doing now.

Having to think all this through, instead of being able to make a case as any doctor would understand it, and leave it at that, must seem very irritating. One day we may have managers who do understand the clinical world better than many do now, but they will never be able to be experts in all the medical specialties and they have a different perspective for good reason: their priorities are different because their job is different, as well as their training. So, they may be balancing the resource needs of a whole hospital and short-term needs against longer-term developments and the wider context of government policy and changes in the region.

One way to short-cut the need for lengthy study of managers' perspectives and careful preparation of three step cases, is to develop the relationships. If doctors can get their managers to trust them as someone who is honest and well-intentioned, they may be able to save lengthy negotiations. To gain this trust does take time, and is not helped by managers' frequent moves, but it can be speeded up. The essence of developing trust seems to be openness from doctors, showing more of themselves: hopes and fears, successes and worries.

Underlying this approach to managing others, lies a perception of oneself as part of the problem, which was discussed in Chapter 6. It is easy to blame Hugh, or the chief executive in Jane's story. Doubtless both had their faults, but Jane could not change them. What she could do was come to see how she might not be handling them in the best possible way and how her own failings might be harming her concerns.

The important messages in this chapter seem to be:

- seeing one's assumptions is key and others can help you do that
- the logical case is unlikely to secure approval on its own
- you need to understand and manage those above you
- developing relationships of trust can save time in the long run

References

Gabarro JJ, Kotter JP. Managing your boss. *Harvard Business Review* May-June 1993

McGill I, Beaty L. *Action Learning.* 2nd edn. London: Kogan Page, 1995

Riley J. The mirror group. *HSJ* 19 Oct 1995, pp. 28–29

CHAPTER 11

Reflecting on What We Have Learned

In this chapter I want to summarise what we are beginning to see that we have learned from working with doctors. Much of what I have to say is no more than speculation but it seems that others who work with doctors share many of my hypotheses.

First, I want to draw attention again to the situations that doctors often seem to find difficult, such as:

- time management
- communication problems
- difficult people
- wicked problems
- personal fears.

I shall suggest reasons why those situations are so commonly found to be difficult and put that explanation in the context of how medical and managerial practice is changing. I shall suggest that these difficulties are linked and find their sources at least partly in how doctors are trained and the nature of their clinical work.

Time management

Doctors often ask for help with time management if they are surveyed on their choice of topics for a management course. In Chapter 4 we had the story of the medical directors having great difficulty in choosing priorities for their efforts. Almost all the doctors I have met through the King's

Fund have spoken of their stress and attributed it to having too much to do. They have other sources of stress, such as difficult decisions or worries about the quality of services, but it is working long hours and feeling it is never-ending that really seems to be hard. Yet it is also possible that working long hours is a way of defending oneself against noticing and having to tackle, or cope with. the extremely difficult nature of many doctors' decisions.

As I suggested in Chapter 4, there could be an explanation for this phenomenon in the way that doctors have to behave in their clinical management. Much of their time is controlled by others, such as clinic managers or receptionists, as well as patients, and doctors have to learn to respond to all the work that is sent their way. It would be unprofessional to refuse to see a patient or to respond to a junior's request for urgent help. This socialisation into becoming work-accepting is heavily emphasised, I would suggest, during training, when house officers are encouraged to work enormously long hours and to cope when truly exhausted.

In managerial work, there is much less control of one's day-to-day agenda by others, at least at the level at which most doctors enter it. Managers learn to prioritise their own work, to make sensible use of their time and to protect themselves from overwork, for no-one else will do it for them. They learn early in their careers to put every problem through at least three hoops:

- Is this my problem?
- Is there anyone else who can help?
- Is it worth giving it time, compared to my other priorities?

General managers rarely understand clinical work, with the exception of ex-nurses. Only rarely do managers have work of the urgency of a clinical case and they do not think to help doctor-managers by scheduling their management meetings to fit round clinics, ward-rounds or surgeries. Doctors, used to accepting the work that is sent, rarely feel able to question the timing of such meetings, or the priority of management tasks that they are asked to do. Doctors balancing private practice with their NHS roles, may be more used to controlling their own time.

Communication problems

In Chapter 5 we had the story of the clinical directors who did not trust their managers or each other and who were unused to sharing their reactions. Many senior doctors seem extremely isolated and find the chance to share their problems in learning sets (as Chapter 8) a huge relief. Others come to us for individual coaching, as in Chapter 7 and seem to need as much the space and attention to talk out their plans to an interested face, as much as any direct advice or coaching.

As I suggested in the discussion section of Chapter 5, it is easy to understand why such difficulties build up, for senior doctors rarely have opportunities for much co-operation with other doctors. They have had to learn to be authority figures for others and in the past were trained to assume that patients wanted to feel confident in their clinical expertise. It is hard to drop such attitudes, even when multi-disciplinary working and partnership with patients are officially approved. Senior doctors have also had to learn how to compete for resources and a competitive stance is not the ideal basis for co-operative behaviour. Their career structure favours competitive people and selects for ability to lead a firm or a practice from the front. Even constructive help can be rejected by such professionals, as it has associations of criticism and messages of insufficiency.

Communication between doctors and managers is often attempted by sending each other written letters, notes and reports. This seems a mistake. Doctors complain of the amount of paper-work (managers do too) and one suggested to me that doctors may not believe problems are real unless they are presented face to face. So the budget crisis may be ignored if it is communicated in the form of an urgent paper for the board: it has not arrived like a patient for a consultation. In addition, communication is hindered by differences of jargon and methods.

In managerial work and among other professions, communication is also often a problem but there has perhaps been more emphasis on team working and team-development. I wonder if there may be a reluctance to draw doctor members of teams into a supportive relationship, from a sense of status differences: the British are still so affected by subtle differences of class and senior doctors are still usually from a higher class than the rest of an executive team. We often have doctors and managers working together and find many signs of mutual anxiety.

Difficult people

Chapter 6 told the story of Frances which, among other things showed us difficulties with different personalities. Chapter 7 had a GP who also saw another person, her senior partner, as impossible. It is very common for doctors to talk of difficult individuals: usually other doctors, but also often senior nurses, managers or other professionals. This is the layman's view of relationships, perhaps combined with the doctors' training to work things out for themselves. Doctors have not been taught to look for alternative views to their own, nor to see themselves as potentially part of any relationship problem. They rarely have had any explanation of how one's own personality and needs may affect how one sees and reacts to another person. They are surprised at first by the idea that people differ and hence may like to work differently (see Chapter 9), and that 'difficult people' may be expressing this diversity, rather than being awkward for the sake of it. Many of the people doctors have to work with are like themselves, also stressed: tired and in a hurry, not too ready to communicate their own problems. Consequently it is all too easy for some of these encounters to go sour and then for each to assume that the difficulty lies in the other person and is a permanent feature of their character.

Perhaps one of the reasons for such difficulties lies in doctors' subconscious dependence on their authority. The world that doctors live in, as they train and gain promotion, is one of deference. Within medicine, there is a clearly defined hierarchy of status, as the doctor passes the barriers of examinations and appointments committees and wins more responsible and senior posts. Patients still mostly adopt the grateful and dependent role. Nurses usually provide reinforcement of the authority of the doctor and most other staff are not going to challenge the doctor in our class-conscious society: the secretary, receptionist, records clerk, porter, cleaning or catering staff. These are less well-paid, less well-educated people, who respect the white coats.

However, once the doctor takes on managerial roles and has to negotiate with managers and other professionals, they find that these people will not necessarily assume that the doctor's managerial decision is right, or that the doctor's wishes must be respected. So, for example, the psychiatrist clinical director may be challenged by the clinical psychologist, refused information by the head of estates, and told she will have to wait to see the head of personnel. Such behaviour is difficult for many doctors to understand and accept. They do not understand why others want to challenge them or be so unhelpful and they are shocked by such unusual behaviour.

We find that this problem is not confined to doctors. Most other professionals also lack the training that might encourage them to construe such difficulties differently. I suspect we could learn a great deal from study of European health care managers and business leaders, who are commonly professionals first. Even managers, who have often had courses in social psychology, do not apply it in the heat of the moment and instead label others, often of course, doctors, as difficult. The NHS has been said to encourage a 'blame culture'. Finding someone to blame can be a healthy way of coping, as long as it does not disable you from trying to tackle problems appropriately. As multi-disciplinary team-working becomes a reality for more doctors and medical education begins to prepare them for this, perhaps these perceptual gaps will shrink. The easy stereotyping of whole professions, or the over-simplistic labelling of individuals as difficult, will surely become less common and more commonly be questioned.

Wicked problems

In Chapter 8 I discussed the concept of 'wicked problems'. Many of the situations that doctors bring us, while having a wide variety of presenting problems, seem to me to be of this type underneath. The doctor may say, this is difficult because it is a merger, or it's about quality, or getting people to change, yet the conventional wisdom for managing mergers, quality improvement or changing practices does not seem helpful. These problems lie within complex situations of great uncertainty and affecting many interest groups, who do not always share the same information, let alone the same values.

I wonder if part of the difficulty is that doctors have to solve problems, they have to make treatment plans, even while recognising complexity and uncertainty. It is their job to take action, but perhaps we may see less interventionist attitudes in younger doctors. We sometimes now hear from wise GPs, who have trained their patients to accept a deal of 'wait and see'. Not acting is hard for anyone and often a sign of maturity and wisdom. Many managers also struggle with their urge to action, which perhaps becomes less helpful as they move up into the 'dustbin lids' (see page 62) of their organisations. Managers also accept being unable to solve all problems as a standard part of their life. Doctors are often asked into management to help with strategic thinking and decisions and this may be the most frustrating arena for them, as it is where concrete plans for action are becoming less useful, although still demanded by government. Many doctors' instincts tell them that managers who cannot solve managerial problems must be dumb!

I was once coaching a clinical director, whom I shall call George, with whom I developed two catch phrases, 'Watch out for A to B thinking' and, 'Is that the leader's job?' By 'A to B thinking', we meant his tendency to see the answer to every question as soon as the question appeared, without allowing himself a moment to consider any complexities, uncertainties or others' interests. So, when letters to GPs were delayed because the secretaries were overloaded with research reports, George issued rules to the consultants and the secretaries about academic work not being done by NHS secretaries. It was an obvious answer and he was surprised when it was not effective. However, I only had to suggest that it might be a bit more complicated than he had thought and to prompt him with questions like,

* Who holds the power?
* Who cares about the letters?
* What did those involved think of his rules?
* What solutions did they prefer?,

for him to see much of the possible complexity that he had been missing.

When he was worrying about his own work overload and tiredness, we got into the phrase, 'Is that the leader's job?' to express his instinctive leaping into inappropriate work. It came to us through a different problem he had: he resented a clinically excellent and conscientious consultant who 'will not manage his department'. As we talked it over, it became clear that George was quite rightly worried that the administrative staff and the nurses in this department were not being managed. When I asked him whose job that should be, he was also clear that that should be the service manager's job. In this particular case, the service manager had been unwell for some months and there were questions of her competence, which had made it particularly difficult for George to ask for her help.

George explained that he saw the problem but felt diffident about invading managerial territory and so instinctively looked for action within his own doctor group. He realised that he did this a great deal and that this reluctance to delegate problems, or ask for help with areas that he judged to be unsatisfactory, combined with his urge to instant action, was enormously increasing his workload. He was doing a lot of other people's work, because he saw his job as managing as well as leading. The idea that the clinical director job might be shifting from taking responsibility for controlling budgets, was an interesting one for George. The notion of shifting to a clinical leader, as many trusts are now doing, was extremely heartening. He loved the strategic management or leadership, he hated and was not very good at detailed people management. He could enjoy creating and choosing between alternative directions for his directorate. He must learn to keep out of other people's areas of responsibility but to ask them to help when clinical quality was becoming threatened.

In George's story four common areas of difficulty come together:

- He had overt problems in managing his time
- He found communication with others difficult
- He tended to blame whole groups, rather than seeing it was individuals he found difficult
- He tended to see only the surface of complex problems and jump into inappropriate action.

Personal fears

When doctors trust us and feel safe enough to talk about some of their real fears about moving into managerial work, we hear many more personal doubts and difficulties which might be summed up as 'Do I really want to do this?' They expect to become less trusted by peers and to suffer more isolation from having 'gone over to the enemy'. They worry about their ability to manage their time with the extra tasks. They worry about their capacity for these new tasks. They worry about the effects of such a step on their longer-term careers, very aware of how easy it is to get out of date. Later, if they take on a part-time management post, they may worry more about how to give up the excitement and feeling of stimulation, the challenges and the sense of having real power for good, that management work can bring!

These fears are all quite justified. Doctors tell us of complaints from their peers and of colleagues becoming less friendly and the ensuing feeling of isolation they experience. As I noted above, nearly all managerial doctors suffer from overwork and are seriously stressed by the pressures on their time. While many are happy to return to wholly clinical posts, a percentage do have difficulty in career planning after a spell in managerial work. I think that these difficulties are particularly strong for doctors because they do not instinctively talk of such things. They have learned to hide their feelings and to put them aside, for the benefit of others. They do not communicate easily about their own problems and expect (and are expected by others) to solve their problems themselves.

While a manager might have similar personal problems, they might be more likely to find colleagues to talk to, or want and know how to get personal or career counselling. However, we meet many chief executives and other senior managers who confess to being extremely isolated, especially at times of acute stress. Doctors are often appalled at managers being told to 'clear their desks'.

Time management	Work load controlled by others Work accepting attitude
Communication	Being the authority figure Competing for resources
Difficult people	Unaware of nature of relationships Unaware of own role Unaware of differences of style
Wicked problems	Action-oriented attitude Problems must be tackled
Personal fears	Isolation Ignore emotions attitude

Figure 11.1 Summary of common difficulties

The summary table in Figure 11.1 suggests that some of these difficulties can be connected – my hypothesis is that doctors, both because of their training and because of the nature of their clinical work, hold some attitudes that make managerial work particularly difficult.

Working with professionals other than doctors has led me to see that they share many of the same difficulties in taking on managerial work. Probation officers, social workers, accountants, nurses and academics all have difficulty with this transition, whether they become full-time managers or try to run both roles at once. Much successful management development rests on enabling them to mobilise their own profession's skills and approaches to themselves, their staff and colleagues. However, for each profession there seem to be some attitudes that are essential for their profession but which do not transfer well to management. In those areas instinctive reactions may not help, indeed they may make things worse.

Some shifts in these attitudes may be occurring – for example, towards a less authoritarian stance in relation to patients and the other clinical professions. Consequently, the shift into a managerial role may not be so hard for some doctors in the future. We are starting to see this already, among the contacts we have with senior registrars, who seem to be more ready than the older doctors we meet, to share responsibility and think in terms of teamwork. Older doctors often complain that junior doctors have a much less selfless commitment to their work – which might translate into fewer problems with overload and exhaustion in the future.

Doctors who take on managerial roles have to combine working in two quite different cultures, which involve them in making different assumptions. Both work for the same organisations within a broad NHS culture but there are striking differences for the two groups. These could be summarised as follows:

The doctor's world	The manager's world
• Focused on the individual patient	• Focused on population groups
• Has contact with patients face to face	• Rarely meets patients or families
• Expected to solve all presenting problems	• Has to choose which problems to tackle
• Learned to be independent and competitive	• Expects to share responsibility with others
• Trained to emphasise the scientific approach	• Has to remember political factors and human motivations
• Expects problems to have solutions	• Expects to have to tolerate many insoluble problems
• Expects to stay with the same trust for whole career and has job security	• Has to move to gain promotion or to cope with redundancy
• High social status with professional freedoms	• Medium social status and subject to bosses

CHAPTER 12

Do It Yourself

Unplanned development as a manager

Much development happens by itself, as it were, during your career. Different specialties bring different opportunities for this kind of learning. The following story is about Thomas, a pathologist whose managerial development stemmed from the wide range of different situations that came his way as a doctor and then as a doctor–manager.

Thomas has had no formal management training as such. Like most doctors, his medical training included some management, although it was not labelled as this. For example, his pathology training included examination questions on the running of laboratories – basic health and safety, discipline questions and how to cope with organisations and people. His work as a consultant included much experience on those topics, so the examination learning was not forgotten the next day.

His experience also made him thoughtful about wider aspects of management. He saw how the laboratories' role affected the rest of the hospital and the local GPs. At a time of increasing concern about costs, labs led the way in knowing how much things cost. Fighting to secure resources for his own service, he challenged waste and large catch-all budget items, such as 'Medical and Surgical Other'. Managers began to notice him, thinking he spoke their language and shared their aims, although his real concern was to protect the labs.

Technical changes meant that he wanted new equipment for the labs and had to work out how to secure the funds at no extra cost, by veering between budget headings. He learned how to influence the system, when wanting to negotiate a tender to do something entirely new (screening for childhood hypo-thyroidism). He learned not to expect a letter making the logical case to do the trick, but rather to find allies for the idea of a neo-natal screening lab, getting health visitors, paediatricians and nurses to sign up to it. His sense of the inter-relatedness of other professions in a system grew, and he saw how he could protect his area by linking it into others – a whole system is better protected against cuts.

Political changes meant restructuring the labs with job losses and rising fears of change among the MLSOs. Working as head of pathology by now, he gradually learned how to help by,

> 'Keeping my gob shut and listening, not just to let them dump all their worries but to understand them. Then I could point out "the key concern you have is ... and we might resolve that this way ..." That way I secured win-win solutions. I had to explain the vision, the trends, that things would never be the same again but that we could win if we kept ahead of the game and were not just reactive.'

Over the years, he reckoned his staff gradually changed their attitudes, so that, for example, when he proposed franchising the service ten years later, the reactions were generally positive, 'We'd rather do that than lose our jobs'. Everyone saw it as fair, even if they did not get what they wanted individually.

Thomas had always been interested in education and as a clinical tutor, studied small-group techniques. He saw that he could use these as part of his management style so, for example, in his meetings he would jot the main points down on the whiteboard, which seemed to be appreciated. He came to see management of change as largely a matter of educating others to see the need for, and how to achieve, sustainable change.

Within the national association of clinical tutors, he wanted to build a new professional organisation. He watched and thought about influence in meetings and learned how to get his points through – talking to others before the meeting, getting them to seed his ideas into the meeting, tipping people off on where to sit and when to nod agreement. *'You don't get anywhere by banging on. If people don't take your idea, the chances are that you're not looking at it from where they are. I've learned to retreat, to regroup, to take it another way, to disguise it, get someone else to chair it.'* He achieved a building, a secretariat, model job descriptions and Department of Health funding for an Open University course for his national association. He was becoming known for his committee work.

A part-time role of director of quality for his hospital brought him more contact with a good multi-professional group. His reactions to the proposals for NHS reforms were so strong that he was one of a group of 12, who together developed an alternative White Paper. This took him to the local MP and eventually to a meeting with the Secretary of State. This process of reinventing the proposals, even though most of the group's ideas (such as the need for collaboration between purchasers and providers) are only now filtering into the changes, taught him much about working at the political scale. He came to see the inevitability of change and the wide range of influences on it.

Another initiative was to use his study leave for a part-time MSc in Education, aiming for an eventual postgraduate dean post (which he has now secured). One of the many things he learned on this course was quite personal. He is now prepared to confess that at first he found himself horrified by the presence of nurses and physiotherapists on the course, worrying that this meant the intellectual quality of the whole would be low. In fact he discovered their presence, *'Was the biggest strength of the whole thing'.* He told me of swapping roles with a physiotherapist in an exercise, so that she played the consultant and he played the physio.,

> *'I learned more in those four minutes about understanding others' positions... Later, when I worked at the RHA for a while, I found I remembered it and could see both sides. This ability to understand how others are seeing the world has stood me in good stead ever since. For example, I came to see that people who shouted loudly against audit were often those who were on the verge of not coping.*

There was a specialist who was not keeping up-to-date and another consultant colleague who was doing too much private practice ... Their noise and anger were not really a fundamental disagreement with audit at all, but more of a cry for help'.

Seeing it like that made it much easier to manage their opposition.

It may be worth thinking through your own career in the same way that I asked Thomas to do for me:

- Did you learn anything about managing people in your initial training?
- Did your subsequent experience with patients or staff teach you more?
- What have you learned about how to secure resources?
- Have you learned how to influence groups or meetings?
- Have you had to manage significant change in your firm, practice or department?
- Have you gained from any experience outside your main employing organisation?
- Have you any experience that has helped you to be able to see others' points of view?

Self-development as a manager

If you want to try some 'do-it-yourself' management development, you could start by taking a pause, in order to reflect and conduct a brief review. In an hour to yourself, you can check whether you share any of those five common difficulties listed on page 3.

Some of the simple techniques and tools seem to be most welcome to doctors; these are multi-purpose aids to quiet thinking (see Figure 12.1).

Technique	Reminder diagram
Forcefield analysis	see page 32
Stakeholder analysis	see page 32
Urgency/importance matrix	see page 45

Figure 12.1 Management techniques and tools

Similarly, there are a few questions that seem extraordinarily powerful. We all have our own versions of these and we all also often use a quiet, 'Why?' to indicate doubt or to prompt further reflection. Picking a few relevant questions from our top ten provides another quick aid to thinking about a doctor's own situation:

Q   What are you feeling and what does that tell you about what's going on?

Q   Is there anything going on 'under the table'?

Q   Where are you on the change curve?

Q   Have you considered all four options for change?

Q   What would a good doctor-manager do now?

Q   What have you failed to ask or communicate?

Q   Are you trying to rush into a decision or action too soon?

Q   Is this your responsibility and could anyone else help you?

Q   Are you managing in all four directions?

Q   Are you paying attention to all the television channels?

Figure 12.2 Really useful questions for most situations

Co-consulting

Even more powerful is to think with a good listener to hand. There is a technique called co-consulting, which is designed to maximise the benefit of having a colleague's attention to your problems. The technique has the great advantage of needing no preparation. It may be easiest to arrange co-consulting with a close colleague but there can be advantages in asking someone from a different specialty and another organisation.

A common pattern is to meet for a couple of hours, somewhere where the pair cannot be interrupted or overheard. Each time they meet, they bring their diaries and arrange another meeting to suit themselves – every 2–3 months suits many pairs.

When they meet, they settle themselves with five minutes of up-dating and social chat. Then they divide the remaining time between them and put a watch out on the table. Each person's session would then look rather like a monologue, with the talker having at least 90 per cent of the air-time in their session.

The talker explains out loud to their partner about whatever area of difficulty they feel is most pressing. They explore it freely for their own benefit, rambling rather than trying to give a neat explanation. Potentially useful aspects are:

- Explain why it is important to their organisation and to them
- Who is involved? What would they say if they were here?
- What have they already thought of doing?
- What is blocking them from moving forward on it?

When it is their turn to be the listener, their main job is to give good silent attention: eye-contact, looking interested, body facing the talker. They may not need to say or ask anything at all and should certainly not speak for more than 10 per cent of the talker's time. They should avoid judgement at all costs, and advice, unless they are asked for it specifically. If they feel sure that the talker needs some assistance, it may help to:

- Suggest they try one of the three techniques in Figure 12.1
- Ask them a few of the questions in Figure 12.2
- Act as a mirror: tell the talker what they are hearing and observing
- Show them their assumptions – the box that limits their thinking

Reflection and self-awareness

These techniques and questions are essentially aimed at helping doctors to become both 'reflective practitioners' (see Chapter 7, page 81) and self-aware. These seem to me to be the two keys to the philosophy that is emerging in our work. They lie behind what proves to be most effective, what prompts the most gratitude and enthusiasm from doctor-managers.

We do that work with doctors best when we ourselves manage to behave reflectively and to stay aware of our own preferences and reactions.

Doctors' challenges to how we are working can help this process, as long as we do not let ourselves become so defensive that we stop listening to criticism. It sometimes feels like walking a tightrope: I must listen and observe and let myself be open to doubts all the time, but at the same time I must behave confidently and use the experience we have gained to offer what I believe to be likely to be most helpful. I can fall off one side into giving doctors what they are used to, meeting their expectations rather than their preferences and needs. I can create dependency by encouraging confidences and being enormously supportive and clever. I can fall off the other side into serving my own needs to be seen to be clever or entertaining. We usually work in teams and make use of each other and outsiders for supervision to help us stay reflective and self-aware.

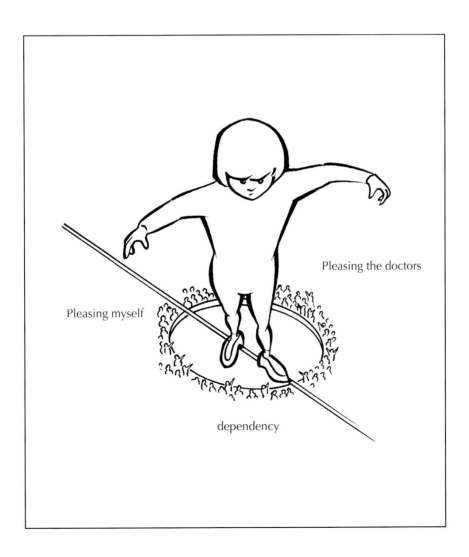

Pleasing the doctors

Pleasing myself

dependency

One last story

My purpose in telling this story is to help any doctor–manager to get an overview of the possibilities and a rough list of criteria they might use to decide what form of management development might suit him better.

M ark rang up and asked if there was a place left on the next 'management course'. He said he had the money, whatever it was, and needed training soon as he had just been made a clinical director. Someone had told him to try the King's Fund and our switchboard had found me for him.

We talked for a little while on the telephone and I mentioned that there might be local training which would be cheaper and had he considered other possibilities than a course? I suggested that we might do better face to face and Mark jumped at that, presumably realising that there was a bit more to the decision than he had thought. He was coming into London the following week for a meeting at the Royal College of Physicians and we agreed to meet when that ended.

The next week he came rushing in at 5.20, embarrassed to be a little later than we'd arranged. When we'd settled into an office with cups of tea, I asked Mark to recap his career for me and to tell me why he had accepted the clinical director post. It emerged that he was on a lot of committees and was interested in the future of his hospital as a whole.

I showed him a list of possibilities that I had jotted down in preparation for his visit:

- ■ MBAs
- ■ National top manager and leadership programmes
- ■ Open University health care management courses
- ■ Regional courses on management for doctors
- ■ Local university/business school courses
- ■ Short courses/seminars
- ■ Learning sets
- ■ Coaching and mentoring
- ■ Workshops for you and colleagues

- Away-days with managers
- Management projects
- Pairing, visits, shadowing
- Reading

We talked through each in turn and it became clear that he was unaware of the range of possibilities: *'Well, I already know more than fifty times as much about this as I did when I came in!'*. He was keen to know dates and costs but I had to explain that I did not have up to date information about all the local possibilities and he would need to try his Human Resources department and ring the NHS Executive's Regional Office, perhaps asking to speak to his local POD, or person in charge of Personal and Organisational Development. I told him there were books, like *Which MBA* that listed details but they tended to go out of date fast so that although they would tell him about local colleges, he would have to ring for up-to-date information.

Mark had young children and a new baby and he warmed to the idea of anything that would avoid too many nights away from home. He let slip that he hated reading when I queried his obvious lack of interest in the Open University courses, so we didn't even discuss the last item on my list.

He got much more enthusiastic when we talked of pairing him with a mentor or with one or more other new clinical directors, with regular meetings every few months to talk over whatever was proving difficult and to share experiences. *'I'd like that, particularly if we could fix the meetings around our own diaries, as you suggest. It's difficult with all these committee meetings.'*

He seemed a quiet rather private kind of person and I guessed that he might gain more from a small group than from the extra contacts that he would get by being in a large course membership. However, he could see that the contacts with managers and other professionals on a mixed course or an MBA would be good. He liked the idea of joining non-health care private sector managers, *'But there's no way my chief executive would cough up nearly £10,000! I hadn't realised you could pay so much.'* He added that he realised that he was a bit nervous of exposing his lack of knowledge in such a group and we agreed that it might be worth thinking about such a course later on when the benefits of having a recognised qualification might be greater, if as he suspected, he might one day want to be a medical director, or even a chief executive.

He could see the value of working with his co-directors and the hospital managers but it obviously felt difficult for him to make that happen from his position as the new boy. *'We do have an away-day planned next month but I think it is to discuss our business plans'.* We talked of how he might want to discuss his own plan with various people in his own organisation and I offered to get a colleague to glance at it if he wanted a quick reaction from someone who had good knowledge and experience of what made for effectiveness.

Mark had not made any notes and I felt a bit worried about how he would remember all this new information. I did not hear from him for six months but then he rang to ask me for help to find a mentor, which I was able to do through another colleague who knew several experienced clinical directors in his area. He reminded me of the regional postgraduate dean, whom I'd forgotten to mention and who my colleague knew was keen to help people in Mark's position.

This story illustrates the very common situation of a complete lack of knowledge among doctors about the different possibilities in management development. We are obviously not too bad at advertising our own courses, they have often been told to ring us but it stops with the concept of a course to pick up some knowledge. However, I do find that doctors are quick to see the possibilities in other ways of securing development and the possible value in contacts and reflecting on their experience and tapping into other doctors' experience. Mentors can however be avoided by some, being seen as potential critics.

The checklist in Figure 12.3 may help you if you are struggling to determine what will suit you best.

Quality issues

A more difficult problem remains that of quality. Not all development opportunities are equally good and I do not know any easy way of checking them out. The British Association of Medical Managers (BAMM) may be able to help and a charity, like the King's Fund or the Office for Public Management, or a university, may give more disinterested advice than a consultancy firm, but sadly these days, we are all keen to take your money.

- Do you like reading? Do you want to study alone or in company?
- How much time away from home can you manage comfortably? Would a modular course help?
- How much money can you afford to spend?
- How important is it to meet other doctors, other professionals, NHS managers, a wider group of non-health care professionals and managers, from the UK or abroad?
- Would a management qualification be useful?
- Have you checked out local possibilities?
- Would reflecting and sharing experience be as useful as a course of knowledge?
- Would it be possible and useful to be with your own colleagues and management team?
- Do you prefer thinking alone or need space to reflect with a bit of help, rather than anything more organised?

Figure 12.3 Checklist of criteria for choosing a form of development

If you find something that looks relevant you might:

- Ask them whether you can talk to someone who has used them before – ask for a list of participants/former clients
- Check their qualifications – you may not be happy if they are not able to match your intellectual weight.
- Ask them how long they have been in business – look for serious experience over several years in helping your kind of person and situation.
- Beware extravagant claims to be able to solve all your problems, look for modest realism and a willingness to share their uncertainties with you.
- Beware offers of the latest and newest!

Doctors who have had a considerable amount of management training, of which there are now a good number, might consider choosing development in a mixed group, with managers and other professions. Opportunities to meet doctor executives from other countries can be useful. Business school courses usually offer a chance to work with managers from other parts of the public sector, or with business people. There are also an increasing number of specialised courses, depending on diagnosis of the individual doctor's preferred areas for development, such as our own psycho-dynamic programmes which emphasise learning about oneself and one's effects on other people.

Many people engaged in management development for doctors care a great deal about the effectiveness of their work and will be generous in helping you to find what will suit you. Most of them care passionately about the quality of their own work for you and genuinely want to help. However, my last word of advice must be to ask you to be intelligent about this, as you would about buying anything, or investing your effort into a new venture.

References

Argyris C, Schön D. *Organizational Learning II: Theory, method and practice*. Reading (Mass.): Addison Wesley, 1996

Economist Intelligence Unit. *Which MBA?* Reading (Mass.): Addison-Wesley, 1993